Celebrating the

An Anthology in Poetry and Prose

By Pen & Keyboard Writers

B.S. Adamsons

Dorothy Cady

Carla Guthrie

Darlinda Hagens

Holly Jahangiri

Eva M. Mahoney

E.H. McEachern

Donna Castle Richardson

Joe Scavetti

Pen & Keyboard Writers is an Affiliate of the
Oklahoma Writers Federation, Inc.

Table of Contents

Preface

Pen & Keyboard Writers is a writing club affiliated with the Oklahoma Writers Federation, Inc.

Members of Pen & Keyboard Writers are authors of published and unpublished novels, short stories, children's books, poetry, and non-fiction. They have a wide variety of interests and experiences, but what they share is curiosity, enthusiasm and support for their fellow writers, and a love of writing.

This book is a collection of poems and short stories that celebrate the seasons - both the four seasons of nature and the parallel "seasons" of a human lifetime. The Pen & Keyboard Writers hope that you enjoy reading their work. Regardless of the number of candles on your birthday cake, their wish is that you may have in your life all the gifts to be presented by each season.

Longing for Four

by Holly Jahangiri

Twigs, encased with ice,
Bending low to hardened earth -
Frost bows to sunlight.
Winter-dormant, seeds
Secreted in soil, nascent,
Spring forth, riotous!
Shimmers on concrete
Belie sultry summer's drought,
Conjure thoughts of rain.
A single red leaf,
Soon joined by gold, brown, yellow,
Blankets sleeping grass.

The Gifts of

Spring

Birth

New Beginnings

Hope

Beginnings

by Donna Castle Richardson

Spring showers bring a smell of fresh air,
As the breeze blows fragrances so rare.

Grass turns from beige to perky green,
Seedlings are peaking upon the scene.

Cherry blossoms present magnificent flowers,
Leading our eyes to view grand towers.

Tulips and daffodils rise into view,
As the world begins to create anew.

Crisp air refreshes the surrounding world.
Sleeping creatures begin to stretch unfurled.

The planet awakens with amazing happiness,
As nature inspires and arouses gratefulness.

Renewed once again to begin creating,
The peaceful world begins awakening.

Start with Spring

by Eva M. Mahoney

It seems to me that our
Gregorian calendar has a serious flaw.
It would be best if the first of the year
happened at the very first thaw.

Not January, in the depths of winter
with cold nights, long and dire.
But, March when we all look at our auspicious goals
we seek and also aspire.

For spring is the time of change,
where the sun is just getting warm.
Where the rain is still cold but cleansing
the dirt from the winter's storm.

Growth all around us commences,
and the dormant all come to life,
To chase the sun's warmth and brightness
And shake off the winter's cold strife.

Evenings are getting shorter
as the daylight exceeds the night.
The spring equinox is upon us
casting, gradually, much more light.

What better time for the New Year to begin,
but when the lamb of March arrives?
And guides us to start anew,
happy to be alive.

Yes, the best reward we earn
for enduring the barren cold winter chill,
is to start our year with the promise of Spring
that shows us nature's goodwill.

Tomorrow

by Joe Scavetti

Carly lay on his bed looking up at the ceiling. The baseball he was tossing into the air fell with a smack into his new Rawlings glove. His free hand propelled the ball up again—smack.

Baseball practice this morning had been tiring. Although the school year had just ended on Friday, the weather was already hot and steamy. It was always hot and steamy in Pensacola. Smack—horsehide met cowhide, again.

His ring tone sounded - the first seven notes of "Take Me Out to the Ballgame"—then repeated as he reached into his pocket for his iPhone. "Hello? Yes, this is Carly..." He hoped he could get past that diminutive form of his name - it was so juvenile. He really wanted to be Carl.

"That's wonderful news, Ms. Frasier—good! I'll be at your office in the morning. Thanks for the call! And for the chance." The job was his. This would be his second summer working at the neighborhood pool. Although it didn't pay much, the work wasn't hard and was one of the few jobs he could do at 14—almost 15—years old.

The news led him into a reverie of comfort and positive thoughts. His dad had been assigned to the Naval Air Station for three years. Carly had actually attended the same school for grades seven through nine. ...a record for him. Being a "Navy Brat" had its downsides but it had advantages, too. At least, that's what Dad always said. Overall, it was a good thing. Dad had a technical rank and basically worked normal business hours.

Working with aircraft navigation software was technical and most of his dad's time was spent teaching in classroom situations. The family wasn't constantly concerned about his safety. He went to work and came home. His dad rarely talked about the job because of security issues.

Again, the ball sailed towards the ceiling and returned—smack. He had just completed his freshman year. In the fall, he and his classmates would go to the high school as sophomores. Grades were never a problem for Carly. Even as he changed from one school to another with his dad's reassignments, he always made good grades. They were never the best grades, but good enough to gain him some respect among the other students.

Sports had been a big factor in being approved by the locals. Some of the kids had actually been together throughout their entire education—they'd never moved. Of course, they weren't military dependents, either.

Church had been a constant for him. The family was able to attend the same denomination churches wherever they lived. Different ministers and different parishioners but the same rituals and teachings. Well, except for the two years that Mom and the boys had lived with Grandma during one of Dad's longer deployments. That was years ago.

He was starting his second year as an Altar Assistant. He was proud to have been chosen for that responsibility and served to his very best ability.

Thoughts of Grandma took some of the joy from his feelings. Even over the miles, he had remained close to her. She was in her sixties when she learned to send text messages. She wanted to keep up with her grandsons. He certainly enjoyed the two summers that Teddy and he spent with her in Iowa. Smack. The baseball stopped in the glove. Last April, Grandma had passed on to what she called her "next adventure."

Carly still found it difficult to grasp the concept of death. It happened to those he loved, and the family had to carry on without them.

But then there was Karen with her dark hair, broad smile, and sparkling eyes. He talked with her at every chance he could create, always talking about current events or trivial subjects. He never expressed his feelings—his infatuation with her. That would never do. Being near her was enough for the present. But that was about to change. He glanced at the small black velvet bag on the nightstand. Yes, this afternoon—after the game.

Horsehide headed to the ceiling, hesitated, and started a descent... smack.

"Hey, Carly—you're not going to believe this " Teddy was standing in the doorway talking in a hoarse whisper.

"Carl—I'm Carl."

"Mom and Dad call you Carly." Still talking in the whisper, Teddy shut the door slowly and quietly.

"Well, Mom and Dad can call me whatever they want—they're our mom and dad."

"Listen to me, Carly. I was just downstairs in the pantry getting some treats—here's one for you." He tossed a Rice Krispy bar onto the bed next to Carly. "I could hear Mom and Dad in the kitchen talking. I kept really quiet—they were talking about Dad being reassigned to San Diego!"

This time the baseball missed the glove and bounced, then rolled, across the floor. "What?? NO...not now!" Carly sat up and Teddy saw his bother's face turn pale.

"Shhhh!" Teddy held a finger up to his lips. "Not so loud. We're not supposed to know about this. I overheard it by accident."

"When are they planning to tell us—after we move?"

"Mom told Dad that she would make our favorite supper tonight and we'll have a family discussion then."

Carly swung his legs over the edge of the bed. Disappointment and anger vied to lead his parade of hormone-driven emotions. "There's not much to discuss. We don't have any say at all. We do whatever our parents want to do... and they do whatever the Navy wants Dad to do." He began to pace around their bedroom.

"Mom and Dad always do what's best for us, Carly. They love us." Carly realized that one of the most irritating things about Teddy as a younger brother was always being right. He saw things that others didn't even notice and could usually make the best of any situation.

"Okay, I can believe that – but so many things in our lives will have to change if we move." Carly continued to pace.

"What's in the black bag?" Teddy was already opening the drawstring closure. "Wow—let me guess—this is for Karen, isn't it?" He was holding a silver bracelet with one charm attached. "A baseball—with your uniform number engraved on the back. That's cool."

"I don't think it will sweep her off her feet, but I want her to have it. Are you going to the game with me?"

"Don't think so...do you mind if I stay home? I really want to go next door and play computer games with George."

"Of course not. It's my ballgame—my friends. Coach said yesterday that I could be the starting pitcher today. We'll see how that goes."

"Whatever you do, don't let Mom and Dad know that I know we're moving. Act surprised."

"Don't worry—I'm not talking about this with anybody. I'll cover for you." Carly playfully punched his little brother in the shoulder. "We guys have to stick together."

Teddy smiled as he thought about that and dashed out the door. Carly heard him bounding down the stairs two at a time. A pending move didn't seem to affect Teddy. Maybe he was too young to remember how hard it had been to start life over in a new town, in a new school among strangers.

He picked up the ball from the corner where it had rolled into and put it on a shelf. It was too early to change, but he laid his baseball uniform on the foot of the bed. He took his cleats from the closet floor and put them and his glove into a nylon gym bag. Before zipping it shut, he stuffed the black velvet bag into an inside pocket. He thought how stupid he had been in buying the charm bracelet. He now realized that he was hoping to buy Karen's affections with a trinket that meant more to the giver than it would to the receiver.

He moped around the bedroom—fretting over the changes he could see, yes dread would befall the family with relocation. Well, mostly he worried over the things about to change in his own life. Emotionally down, he began playing Candy Crush on his iPhone.

"Carly, don't you have a game this afternoon?" Mom's voice drifted up the stairs.

"Yes, I do, Mom. I'm getting ready." All innocence, he thought. She didn't sound like a person who, in the next few hours, would be announcing major changes in his life. He checked the time on the phone's screen—yep, time to get ready.

Since the field was only three blocks away, he usually walked. Sometimes he rode his bicycle. Today he chose to walk. The temperature seemed a bit cooler than the morning. An overcast seemed to be moving in from the south. Cloud cover was a good thing.

Carrying his gym bag, he walked along a dusty path from the house then reached the paved sidewalk across the street. His thoughts weren't on the game, although it was important. This was to be the first game of the season against the Sharks—another Babe Ruth League team from the east side of Pensacola. Last year, his team finished the schedule tied with the Sharks for the city title. The Sharks won a playoff but then lost to Tampa in the first round of the state tournament.

His thoughts were about baseball in general. Carly enjoyed the League play including full-sized diamonds with ninety-foot baselines, metal cleats, and professional regulation baseballs. By turning fifteen in a few weeks, this would be his last summer of eligibility. At least, it would have been. Now it seemed he wouldn't get to play the rest of the current season. San Diego had a major league team but he had no idea about junior leagues. This might be the end of his playing career.

Several players were at the field when he arrived. Family members were settling into the open wooden bleachers. Carly waved at David and set about changing his shoes. He took out the glove and put his Nikes into the bag. David was a skilled catcher and the twin brother of Karen. Usually, Karen and some of her friends came to the games. That was convenient for hanging out and drinking Cokes afterwards. He surveyed the bleachers as he tied his shoes. Karen wasn't there.

"Hey, David. Is your sister coming?"

"She said she would. Usually does. Are you ready to throw a few? Coach said you'll probably be the starter today."

"Yep. I'll burn some holes in your glove."

Other players and fans continued to drift in as Carly walked to the pitcher's mound and tossed a few throws to loosen the muscles of his right arm. "Ya ready, Dave?" He was ready to step-up the pace and throw some breaking pitches.

"Go for it, Carly. Show me what you've got today" A cool breeze drifted across the field from the south. It felt good.

That's when she walked into the stands. Karen was there. She wriggled the fingers of one hand in a sort of silent wave. Since she was walking behind her brother, Carly knew the wave was meant for him alone. Her smile was heart warming. Then he saw Clifford. Karen had come to the game with Clifford—of all people. In the process of throwing when he saw Clifford, the pitch went wide of the plate.

"Hey, I'm over here. The white thing on the ground is the plate." Dave ran to the backstop to retrieve the ball and said a few words to his sister.

Carly's heart was heavy. Karen had chosen to be with Clifford—the defensive tackle on the junior varsity football team. In anger and disgust, Carly remembered a comparison one of his classmates had used last fall. "The only difference between Clifford and the tackling dummy used in practice is that Clifford wears a uniform."

Large drops of rain began splatting into the dust on the field. Carly looked up and was surprised at how dark the sky had become. An afternoon rain was usual along the Gulf Coast but these clouds were really menacing. Usually, the showers only lasted a few minutes and then the sun returned.

Carly had lost his interest in warming up. He motioned for David to follow him to the dugout. There they could get some protection from the rain until it stopped. Although called a "dugout," the facilities were just a covered bench for players to sit on, surrounded by metal fencing.

The two umpires had just arrived and were walking onto the field ahead of a crowd of Sharks players ducking for the cover in the other dugout. The rain increased. "We may be in for it, Carly." David looked at the clouds. "Yep, this isn't the daily shower." As if taking a cue from the catcher's words, the clouds emptied even more rain onto the field. Fans scurried to the shelter of the concession stand or back to their cars.

Watching the skies, the two umpires stood in the doorway of the opposing dugout. A flash of light and a sizzling sound came from overhead—followed by a loud clap of thunder. That was enough for the lead umpire. No games during lightning. The game was cancelled.

The rain continued to pour as the Sharks dashed back to their vans and SUVs. Carly just sat on the bench in dejection. It was over. His chance to pitch—and his hopes of a relationship with Karen. He spoke pleasantries and waved to his teammates as they left the semi-shelter of the dugout for cars or home.

Sitting alone, watching the raindrops dissolve the dust into mud; he waited for the rain to slack. Fifteen minutes later he was the only person left in the dugout. The concession stand was closed and the parking lot was empty. Carly felt empty, too. All those wonderful feelings he had enjoyed just a few hours ago were gone.

He changed his shoes as the wind blew rain through the chain-link fence onto his back. With his bag packed, he started the walk home. Only three blocks away, yet, he envisioned a walk of miles.

As he stepped out of the shelter, the rain instantly soaked his cap and uniform. He hoped the gym bag would keep his glove dry. The rain either mirrored or created his mood. He wasn't sure which. Nothing was going right. His family was relocating—again; his favorite girl was with another guy; the best summer baseball season of his life was ending, and he didn't get to pitch.

All of his hopes, dreams and comforts he enjoyed were, in a day, in an afternoon, being washed away. The things he loved about life were flooding down the storm drains of Pensacola to be lost in the all-consuming sea.

Clouds of depression filled his mind; heaviness filled his heart; and water filled his Nikes as he plodded ahead.

"Into every life some rain must fall, Sugar." That had been Grandma's pet name for Carly.

"Grandma? But this can't be. You're..." He looked around but couldn't see anyone. The rain was too heavy. No one was nearby.

"Dead. Am I real? Am I here? Does it matter? I can't give you a hug, but I want to give you some encouragement. The rain is in your life today and that's all you can see. I want you to keep in mind that tomorrow is coming.

"Tomorrow isn't a single day. Tomorrow is every day of your future. The rain will stop. The clouds will part. We can't see the rainbow when the rain is still falling, you know.

"Tomorrow there will be other leagues, seasons and games. Tomorrow there will be young ladies who will be charmed to wear your uniform number on their bracelet—and one will be proud to wear your ring.

"Tomorrow there will be jobs and a career. There will be honors for service and academic achievement. Tomorrow there will be all the things you feel you're losing, and more.

"Remember that you are loved by many people and that you're not alone."

"Grandma, I..." He sensed that she was gone; the connection, whatever it had been, was no longer there.

Carl felt lighter. The clouds in the sky and those in his mind were clearing. He would accept the relocation and the loss of his comfort zones as a challenge—an adventure.

Yes, he would believe in Tomorrow—his Tomorrow.

Ethan's Springtime Hidden Treasure

by Darlinda Hagens

That same old dreadful feeling washed over eleven-year-old Ethan Butler. Without looking, he sensed the nearness of his stepmother Zona as he spooned up the last bite of his breakfast cereal and pushed the bowl away.

From the round antique kitchen table, he stared out of the large window, noticing the green, open field, and heads of cattle and horses grazing in the distance. Living in the country offered freedom from the overcrowding of city life, but it also offered something more: invisibility. Miles of unobserved activities.

Ethan first started feeling invisible when his father, Conroy, dropped dead from a heart attack last year. Things just never returned to normal. How could they, when his mother passed from a car accident four years before his father's death?

The eleven-year-old never knew what his dad saw in his stepmother. Nothing about Zona came remotely close to beautiful. She wore her hair in a bun at the nape. Her overbite screamed thumb-sucker. And that … that large wart on the tip of her nose. It seemed to grow bigger every day.

Having read sci-fi books to his younger brother, as well as fairytale stories to his sister, Ethan knew what a wart on the nose meant. Witch. Zona carried all the signs. The cackling laughs. The large black pot she used to prepare most of their meals. And the broomstick she hid in the closet.

Any day, Ethan expected her to show her true colors. Then what? How could he protect his younger siblings from her wicked powers?

The first day of Spring, two months ago. Ethan awoke to her standing over his bed, wearing a crooked smile. And the way she said, "Get up, sweetheart." Ethan expected her to throw him into the big black pot.

Since that day, he noticed the subtle changes in his stepmother. He did not know what she secretly plotted, but he felt the deceit of her actions clear down to his toes.

Still, daily she behaved as a holy, meek saint, warmed by Heaven's glory. This morning, same as every school day, she brought the Bible to the kitchen table for him and his two siblings to read.

His ten-year-old brother, Marco, and eight-year-old sister, Journey, finished breakfast. Zona patiently watched as they ate their last bites and pushed their bowls aside.

Walking to Ethan, his stepmother asked, "What's today's scripture?"

He took the offered Bible from her hands and flipped to the passage she seemed to enjoy most. Once he asked her why she liked St. Matthew 13:44 so much. She said, "You never know how God will bless."

Ethan believed that Zona secretly hoped to find her own pot of gold at the end of someone's rainbow. Or something worse, like three fattened children to boil in her pot or roast over an open flame.

After drawing a deep breath, he read, "Again, the kingdom of Heaven is like treasure hidden in a field. When a man found it, he hid it again, and in his joy he went and sold all he had and bought that field."

Zona smiled and went around the table, laying her hands on the head of each child, while whispering prayers.

Her actions always contradicted what Ethan felt in his gut about her. How could he trust a woman who barely shed a tear at his father's funeral?

As Journey and Marco followed Ethan out the front door. Zona made the same speech she made every morning before the children left the porch, "Be careful and prayerful today, my precious pearls. Ethan, you're my dependable one. You're in charge. Marco, as much as I love your adventurous personality, don't let your curious nature get you into trouble. Journey, fearless as you may feel today, the same goes for you. Stay close to your oldest brother."

After promising to obey, all three turned toward the long country road leading to the school. Ethan already accepted the boredom of the walk. He searched the road for rocks to kick to break the monotony. Marco strolled alongside him. When Ethan glanced at his brother, he noted his broad smile and how his eyes darted from place to place, exploring the world around him. Journey, as usual, brought up the rear, keeping pace by flipping cartwheel after cartwheel.

Marco threw out his arms, stopping Ethan in his tracks. Pointing at the dilapidated house on the corner. Marco said, "Someone just looked out the window of that house."

Ethan knew Marco desired adventure, but Zona had warned the children to stay away from this old place. Her warning matched the bold letters on the sign nailed to the wooden post standing in the front yard behind the broken-down fence surrounding the overgrown lawn.

KEEP-OUT.

Reading the look in Marco's eyes, Ethan shook his head. "You know what Zona said about going straight to school?" He glanced back at Journey, who had stopped flipping and now slowly approached them.

"What's going on?" Journey asked.

"Nothing," Ethan shoved Marco in the back. "Let's keep it moving. There's nothing to see here."

"Yes, there is." Marco spun around and spoke to Journey. "The curtain moved inside that old house."

"Really?" Journey grabbed Ethan's arm. "Come on, big brother, can't we at least go into the yard for a closer look?"

"Guys," Ethan used his authoritative voice, "Let's keep walking."

As if Ethan said nothing, Marco eased up to the rickety fence. Journey matched his every step. Ethan followed behind them. "I'm not kidding, if you —" His eyes widened. He questioned if he saw what he thought he did. The once white lacy curtain, now yellowed by age and decay, moved.

"See, I told you." Marco pointed while hopping in place.

All three children gasped as an old woman with long white hair and wrinkles covering every inch of her face flashed a toothless smile. She waggled an extra-long pointy fingernail, beckoning them inside, before moving away from the window.

"Ethan! Journey! Did you see that?" A wide grin spread across Marco's face.

Ethan swallowed the lump in his throat. "Yes. But we are not going in there."

Once again, Marco disregarded Ethan's command and said, "The old lady signaled to us. We can't just ignore her."

Ethan puffed a loud sigh. "You know what Zona said."

"Shouldn't we find out if she needs help?" Journey took a step closer to the fence. "Marco, we should check it out."

"No," Ethan said, "Where's your common sense? You should be afraid instead of asking to go check it out."

Marco fanned his hand. "We live in the middle of nowhere. I've seen stuff way scarier than an old woman in a window. Remember when that mountain lion caught a deer? Now that was scary, I could've been his meal if not for —"

"Okay, I get it. Still, I'm the oldest. Zona said I'm in charge. We're going to school and that's that."

"Can't we wait to see if she comes back to the window?" Marco asked. "Just for a minute?

"If she does, we are still not going into that shack." Showing authority, the older child folded his arms.

They waited.

Seconds ticked by.

Just as Ethan decided their imaginations had run away with them, it happened again.

The old woman appeared in the window, gesturing for them to come inside.

Surprise and fear jolted in Ethan's chest. He stumbled backward, lost his footing, and ended on his butt in the middle of the narrow street. Sitting with his mouth agape, he glanced at Marco, who wore a look of pure satisfaction.

Ethan looked back at the house and yelled, "Stop! Stop!"

Journey ran, disregarding his demands. She climbed over the fence and sprinted full speed to the front door that hung more crossways than perpendicular to the door frame.

Marco turned to Ethan. "I'll go get her."

"No." Ethan hopped to his feet, but he moved too slowly. Marco lifted the rickety latch and ran through the gate.

Although the sun shone brightly, rising high in a cloudless sky, darkness enveloped Journey and Marco as soon as they stepped across the threshold.

Ethan yelled, "Guys! No!" He stood puzzled, wondering how things got out of hand so fast. Then he hurried through the gate after them. Rotting boards cracked under his weight as he stepped on the distorted porch. Fearing, at any second, the whole thing may come crashing down, he tiptoed a crisscross path to the front door.

The sounds of astonishment filtered out to where Ethan stood.

"It's beautiful," Journey said. "Come in, Ethan, you'll love it."

Marco echoed her opinions, "This is better than twenty years of summer vacations rolled into one."

Ethan refused to fall for their tricks. "Either you come out right now or I'm going to get Zona."

"Yeah, go get Zona," Journey yelled, "tell her the Bible scripture you read this morning was true. And this house is proof. It looks like nothing on the outside, but when you step through the door, the view becomes awesome. This is the hidden treasure. It must be Heaven!"

Ethan stood on the porch debating whether to go get Zona or go in and drag Journey and Marco out. Their laughter and cheers spiked his interest. With his hands bracing the sides of the door frame, he stuck his head inside.

His grip loosened as his eyes grew wide, beholding the most vivid colors on earth. A wonderland.

Stairs, which looked like extra-large bars of gold, led up to a roller coaster without tracks. It flew. Weaving from place to place like a giant centipede, it glided under the arch of a rainbow. Various fruit trees floated mid-sky. Birds and butterflies of every imaginable shade perched on branches of their choice.

Marco stood with his hands filled with assorted candies under a bridge made of gingerbread cookies and candy canes, watching a pod of dolphins jump, twist, and land in waves of chocolate milk.

Journey rode high on the back of a Humpback whale with flippers that soared with the finesse of an eagle's wings. His sister snatched pieces from fluffy pink and blue clouds. With her mouth crammed full of the fluff, she said, "It's cotton candy." Laughing and waving, she sailed into the caramel and fudge sunrise.

Ethan scratched his chin. None of this made sense. Still, he never remembered seeing his brother and sister so happy.

Journey pointed toward the front door and the large mammal changed course and floated so close it forced Ethan to duck his head back outside.

Through boggled thoughts, he tried to balance the believable with the unbelievable, but the phenomenon seemed too unnatural. It defied the laws of gravity, and he found no earthly explanation.

At that moment, the old woman in the window appeared beside him. Ethan screamed and jumped back, plastering himself against the decaying siding of the house. The old woman morphed into Zona. Then, before his eyes, the wart hanging on the tip of his stepmother's nose faded. Next, her overbite disappeared. The bun at her nape unraveled into dark, wavey tresses. And a halo appeared above her head. The gold sash circling her waist enhanced an elegant white gown. She looked magnificent, with her beauty on full display.

A soft, loving peace entered Ethan's heart. He walked to her side. "So, I was wrong, wasn't I? You're not a wicked stepmother, are you?"

She smiled. "Consider me your guardian angel. The Merciful One sent me to care for you and your siblings."

Ethan ran his hand over one of her feathery wings. "I don't understand."

"There's lots in this world that humans do not appreciate. Just know that the Creator wants what's best for you. Losing both of your parents fell hard on everyone. But now, it's time, He rewards you and your siblings for your bravery."

She ushered him inside the run-down building. The outside may look like it needed to be condemned, but the inside shouted paradise.

Zona looked Ethan in the eyes. "This is the hidden treasure. We truly do not know how, when, or why God blesses. But always remember, prejudging outward appearances could lead to missed blessings. Miracles come when least expected, in places you could never imagine, from people most would never consider."

Throwing caution to the wind, excitement skidded up Ethan's spine. All his doubts regarding Zona vanished.

At last, he understood. Like this unexpected springtime surprise, most treasures remain hidden in ruins.

Waterfalls

by Dorothy Cady

April 1st, 4:17 p.m.

Shara Keldwyn parted the curtains and moved the steaming teapot to the kitchen windowsill to cool. She knew the teapot wouldn't get her the attention she was looking for, but if her neighbor was right, its steaming contents could. On Saturdays, Mrs. Nathan always put her freshly baked cookies in the window just before the postal carrier, Burt, arrived. He always stopped to compliment her on her baking, which resulted in Mrs. Nathan giving him a cookie or two. But Shara had been in love with Burt for a while now, and she knew with his retiring that today was her last chance. Mrs. Nathan had promised to help.

With the pot balanced on the sill, Shara paused to watch the tepid spring breeze swirl the steam as it rose and carried the spicy scent toward her front door. She took a deep breath and sighed. *I hope this works.* Glancing down the walkway she spotted Burt. Right on time, she thought, as she watched him approach Mrs. Nathan's house next door.

Pulling back from the window a bit so he would not see her watching him, she waited for Burt's reaction as he stepped up to her door. *Would he notice the slight smell or think it too strange to see a plain grey teapot sitting in the window? What if he doesn't have any mail for me today?* Without thinking about it, Shara put her hand on her stomach. It rumbled, but she wasn't sure if it was due to growing hunger or panic. She wished she had a little more experience at luring in a man. As Burt reached her white picket gate and reached down to open it, Shara held her breath and took a step back into the shadows of her kitchen. When he lifted his head, she could tell he'd noticed the strange scent. His eyes searched back and forth then spotted the teapot. Though Burt was respectful enough, he wasn't what Shara would call friendly on most days. So, when she saw the side of his mouth tip up into a half smile, she knew she had his attention. Burt stepped up onto her tiny porch, but instead of opening her black mailbox mounted there, he knocked on the door.

Shara smiled, smoothed her dress, and opened the door. "Why, Burt. It's good to see you. You must have a package for me today."

"Well," Burt said, "not exactly." He drew in a deep breath and nodded towards her kitchen. "That fragrance is so . . . intoxicating. Is it tea? I noticed the pot on your windowsill."

"Yes," Shara said. "It's a new blend, and since you brought me the original box of it a few weeks ago"—which she knew was a lie, but that he wasn't likely to remember a single package delivery—"I thought I might be able to tempt you into having a cup of it with me today. I mean, since it's your last day and all."

Burt looked over his shoulder then down at his bag, lifting it slightly to test its weight. "Looks like I don't have too much left to deliver today. I think I could take a short break." He took in another deep breath. Shara watched the edges of his lips curl up, this time into a full smile.

Shara swung her door wide and stepped back. Before closing the door, she stuck her head out and gave a furtive glance up and down the street. Satisfied at seeing only the neighbor's calico cat digging in its owner's flowerbed, she closed the door then showed Burt to the kitchen table. "Have a seat," she said, retrieving her silver trivet and setting it on the table.

"Wow," Burt said. "Is that really an old Wedgewood Double Oven Stove? My apartment has one similar to it. That's so weird."

"It is," Shara said. She placed two dainty white china teacups with matching saucers on the table, one in front of Burt. Then she retrieved the teapot from the windowsill, closed the window, and set it on the trivet. "I bet yours isn't blood red. I had mine repainted because red's my favorite. Cream and sugar?"

"No thanks. There's sugar enough right here in front of me," Burt said.

Shara noticed that he was staring at her and not showing any sign of embarrassment as he said it. It almost made her feel uncomfortable. *Strange. Was that supposed to happen? I wish I'd had some training before. . . She shook her head to clear it. *Remember why you're doing this. You deserve him. Besides, everything is going as planned.*

Shara, all 103 pounds of her, dropped into the chair opposite from Burt. Her vintage red and aluminum set from the 1950's was another of her acquisitions. She had always romanticized life in that decade because of all of the special things her mother had told her about growing up in that time. When her mom got inoperable cancer and died five years ago, Shara had inherited some of her mom's 50's furnishings. She also had promised her mom that she would find a good man and make her a grandma one day. *He's a good man. I'll keep my promise. Burt will do, right Mom? Please forgive me for the how.*

Shara poured tea for both of them, but hadn't even picked up her cup before encouraging Burt to drink his. "Give it a taste," she told him. "Tell me what you think. It's a new blend for me." Shara's body almost tingled; she hoped Burt could not see the eagerness in her eyes.

Burt lifted the tea cup to his mouth, took a few quick swallows, and then set it back on the table. "I'm sorry, Miss Keldwyn, but . . ."

"Oh please. Call me Shara. We don't need to be formal. Besides, since you are retiring, we probably won't see each other again."

Burt groaned and pushed his chair back. "Thank you for the tea, but I have a schedule to keep. I really have to get going." Burt rose and headed for the front door, grasping the wall for support. His head felt as though his brain had decided to ride an out-of-control merry-go-round. *Must have risen too fast.*

"Wait. Please," Shara said. "You don't look well. Sit back down for a minute and drink your tea. I'm sure it will help."

Burt turned and a single step later he was back at the table staring at his cup of tea. Shara had lifted it to his mouth and was helping him take a small sip.

"Better?" she asked.

"Not much. I'm dizzy and a bit sleepy." Burt recognized that his speech had become slurred, and while the kitchen had been quietly lit with the afternoon sun through the kitchen window, the light now felt blinding. *What's wrong with me? I'm sitting here like a rock stuck in the mud of a spring flood. Something's not right about this. I have to leave. Come on. Move. Go.*

Shara smiled at Burt. She couldn't know exactly what he was thinking, but she was pretty sure by the lack of expression on his face and his dilated pupils that the tea was doing its job. "Drink it all down now, Hon. That's right. It's good for you."

As she watched Burt lower his head to the table, Shara felt a bit guilty.

April 1st, 8:02 a.m.

Despite the backache that his pain medicine had not yet calmed, Burt stepped into his mail delivery van with a smile on his face. After dropping his personal backpack on the floor beside him, he started up the van, put on his seatbelt, and then hit the power button to turn on his CD player. TLC's second album, CrazySexyCool, was already loaded. He switched the track to his favorite song, and started singing along. "Don't go chasing waterfalls, baby. . ." Burt added a rhythmic tapping with his hands on the steering wheel. He tried not to think about the poverty, or his single mom who'd raised him and his siblings by working three jobs.

As he was about to head out, one of his coworkers pulled up next to him. "Hey, Burt," John said. "Will we see you tonight for your retirement party?"

"Definitely," Burt shouted back. "You know me. Any excuse for a Saturday night party." He waved to the man as John pulled away then headed out just behind him, still tapping his fingers to the music.

"Twenty and done" Burt shouted to no one. *I can't believe it's my last day of delivering useless junk mail to people who will likely heave it in the trash before I can walk to the next house. But it's worth it.*

Burt had only two miles to drive before the start of his delivery route, but he waited until he reached his first house before shutting off the music, collecting the mail for this street, and stuffing it into his mail bag. "Only seven hundred and eighty three homes to visit," he said as he stepped out of the van and headed for the mailbox attached to the side wall of the home at 16004 Sunny Day Drive—the first house he went to everyday, and the last time he'd be at this one. *I know everyone thinks I'm crazy to be leaving this job after only twenty years, but hey, they don't have my plan. By the time I actually retire, I'll have multiple sources of income from different pension plans. The postal service is the first, but there will be others.*

Burt slipped the mail into the box, the old lid screeching like a cat that just had its tail stepped on. *Wish she'd put a drop of oil on those hinges. You'd think it would bother the owner as much as it does me, but apparently not.* He sighed and checked his watch. *Maybe I can break my time record today. It's not like I'll get another chance.* He rushed off to the next house, and the next, and the next until he finally reached his last assigned house on Sunny Day Drive. His up-one-side-of-the-street-and-down-the-other approach to mail delivery always ended him back at and just across from his delivery van. He slipped inside, withdrew a bottle of water from his backpack, and gulped down half of it then wiped away the sweat on his forehead. Although it was still early spring, the temperature had climbed into the mid-eighties and had stayed there all week. He drank the last of his water then started the van and headed to the next street.

Burt's day seemed to drag, maybe because it was his last one, or maybe it was the traffic. Saturdays were always the worst day of the week for making deliveries. At least that was true in his area. There were more hazards to look out for on the weekend, like more cars coming and going, more dogs running loose, and even more children riding bikes and playing in the street.

April 1st, 4:11 p.m.

Burt pulled the van to a stop at the head of Malaise Avenue, the final street on his route. He'd always liked this street. It was the only one he traveled that had at least one large, old tree for every house on the block. Today the sun filtered through the tree leaves and stippled the hood of his van with skipping shadows. Despite the weather prediction that today would be the hottest April first in the past ten years, a clement breeze helped to cool him.

Stepping down from the van, Burt checked his watch. *Five minutes less than my best time. That's hard to believe. But I made it here and all I have to do now is to not interact with any of the residents, and I will have beaten my own record. Not that it matters much. But it will give me bragging rights at my party tonight.*

He reached into the van and picked up this street's mail then stuffed it into his leather mail bag. "Let's finish this you trusty old bag, you," he said aloud then snickered. "It's a Wonderful Life" had become his favorite movie when he was young. The whole family had watched it together every Christmas since before he was born. But now, he was the only one of his seven siblings who showed up on Christmas Eve to watch it with his mom. And though he'd never admit it to any of his brothers or sisters, he still watched it all of the way through whenever he was feeling unbearably lonely. I guess a 38-year-old man with brown hair, a scruffy beard, and a slight pot belly was not what every woman around his age was looking for in a boyfriend.

Burt watched for a moment as robins darted in and out of the trees. The crabapple trees in this neighborhood always bloomed early and their yellow leaves tinged in red were beautiful. He pulled in a deep breath of cinnamon-scented crabapple air, and then headed for the corner home on the street. Distracted by pulling out the next stack of mail from his bag, Burt stepped up onto the sidewalk, but didn't lift his foot high enough. He stumbled, caught his balance, and took a quick glance around hoping not to see anyone that might have noticed him. Now I'll really have to hurry, he thought, and I won't have time for Mrs. Nathan's cookies. Oh, heck. No way am I missing those today. Guess I will have to settle for four minutes instead of five, or maybe three. Mrs. Nathan's a talker.

Burt rushed from house to house until, a little winded, he reached Mrs. Nathan's home. He expected that his mail drop off for her would eat up the last of his extra time, but she'd met him at the door then hurried him away with six wrapped sugar cookies that he tucked with care into the outside pocket of his bag. "Congratulations on your retirement, Burt," Mrs. Nathan yelled and waved as Burt walked away. "I'm certain it will be interesting."

Next up was Miss Keldwyn's house. She was a nice enough woman, and pretty, too. The few times he'd seen her, her amber hair was always in a thick braid that almost touched her willowy waist. Once she had even met him at the door and given him a polite smile that showed her dimples. She had never shown any interest in him, but of course, he felt too shy around her to stop and really find out. Most days she would disappear from the kitchen window the moment he swung open her gate. He doubted today would be any different. *Three more houses he reminded himself. . . What is that smell?* Burt took a deep breath hoping to figure out the scent. Glancing around he saw a steaming teapot sitting in Miss Keldwyn's kitchen window. That's different, he thought. I bet whatever that is would go great with my sugar cookies. Maybe I can talk her into having one with me. Burt walked up to Miss Keldwyn's door, ignoring the mailbox, and knocked. So much for avoiding homeowners, he thought. But it smells so good, and I can't resist it; don't want to resist it.

April 1st, 4:32 p.m.

Mrs. Nathan burst through Shara's back door and straight into the kitchen. "Is he alive?" she asked.

Shara reached across the table and put two fingers to the inside of Burt's wrist. Her hand shook. "He is," she said.

"Good. Let's get him downstairs." Mrs. Nathan lifted one of Burt's arms and Shara walked to his other side and wrapped his arm over her shoulder. They lifted then wrangled him into an almost upright position. "Is everything ready?"

"I believe so." Shara nodded. "Two of them arrived early this morning to set up." Grunting, Shara and Mrs. Nathan half walked and half dragged Burt to the basement stairs, and then walked him down them one slow step at a time. Shara could hear clanking noises, like someone setting a dinner table, and felt a bit overwhelmed by the antiseptic hospital smell. The two strangers, both bigger and stronger than Mrs. Nathan and Shara combined, met them at the foot of the stairs and took over. They moved Burt to the gurney and strapped him down. "Will he be alright? Will he remember anything?" Shara asked. The strangers didn't reply, but set to work and had him set up with an IV, oxygen, and monitors in what felt like seconds to Shara.

"Come on," Mrs. Nathan said. She tugged Shara's arm to pull her back upstairs, but Shara resisted. "Wait. You promised."

"I know. They'll take very good care of him; they know what they're doing. And I will make sure they keep their promise to you as well. It will be your turn down here when they are done with Burt," Mrs. Nathan said. "Then only nine months from now, you'll be a mother. That's what you wanted, right?"

Looking over her shoulder towards Burt, Shara asked, "Will they hurt him?"

Mrs. Nathan scrunched up her face for just a moment, but then her smiling, friendly-neighbor look reappeared. She put her hand on Shara's shoulder and said, "Of course not. And remember, the goal is not just one for you, but an extensive collection to help ensure their species future. Now, don't worry; there will be no visible signs of the procedure, no permanent damage, and it's likely he'll never know what happened."

Shara had turned and started up the staircase with Mrs. Nathan right behind her when one of the strangers stopped them. Because he was dressed in black from head to toe, complete with full headgear, Shara could only see the stranger's eyes. There was something rather different about him, but what did she expect? He wasn't exactly human. She hadn't noticed it when they'd first arrived, probably because their attention had been on the gurney they pushed and keeping all of the equipment and things she

50   CELEBRATING THE SEASONS

didn't even recognize from falling off of it as they carried it down the basement stairs.

Shara no longer felt as sure about this as she had before. "How long will it take?" she asked.

"Not too long," the stranger said. "Maybe a couple of hours, if we have no issues. Easily enough time for you to handle your task." He handed to Shara a neat stack of the postal carrier's clothing, shoes, and personal items. "Bring these back when we call you." The stranger turned and went back to the gurney on which lay a now naked Burt. Shara couldn't help but look and admire. She and Mrs. Nathan were both silent as they returned to the kitchen.

"OK. Go get changed. When you're ready, we move on to the next step—plausible deniability."

Mrs. Nathan kept busy in the kitchen, setting up a pot of coffee to brew, and thinking about Shara. *She is too fidgety and unsure to suit me.* Mrs. Nathan sighed. *The young ones are always like that. Maybe one day I will get used to it.* She poured two coffees and set them on the table, just as Shara came out of the room dressed in Burt's clothing. "That looks a bit frumpier than I expected." Mrs. Nathan said. "Turn around, please. . . OK. We'll need to pinch it in here with a belt," which Mrs. Nathan adeptly put around Shara's waist. "Stuff this newspaper into the shoulders." Shara did as instructed. "That's much better, far from perfect, but I think it will do. Just don't let any of the neighbors get a good look at you. Be quick."

Shara walked over to the table and sat down. She took a sip of the hot coffee Mrs. Nathan poured for her, blowing on it first to help keep it from burning her mouth.

"Did you buy the matching colored ball cap I told you to get?"

"Yes." Shara stood partially and pulled it from her back pocket to show it to Mrs. Nathan before putting it on her head.

"That will do. Now, you only have to deliver the mail to two more houses, and then drive his van back to the post office. Try to make sure at least one person sees his van driving away. I have arranged for someone to pick you up and bring you back here. They will be waiting for you when you arrive. Do not dawdle there. We have a limited time to complete the process on you. Understood?"

Shara nodded, grabbed Burt's bag, and headed out the front door. She tried to think about how Burt walked so she could emulate him. She wondered if there was anything special he usually did that made him stand out and recognizable to her neighbors. Then she remembered Mrs. Cavanaugh's dog. Shara fished around in Burt's bag, pushing aside the remaining envelopes and a couple of magazines until she found what she needed. She was glad she had remembered Mrs. Cavanaugh telling her about Burt's first encounter with her two schnauzers and how he had brought Bumblebee and Brambleweed each a dog biscuit every visit since. "We all appreciate the peace and quiet," Mrs. Cavanaugh had said.

As Shara started out the door, Mrs. Nathan stopped her. "Let me have those sugar cookies I gave Burt. I'll dispose of them. We don't want someone finding and eating them. It might raise a few questions."

"Wait," Shara said. "You drugged his cookies?"

"Of course. It was the easiest way to ensure everything ran smoothly. You might call it my backup plan, dear, in case the tea didn't work." Shara set the partially wrapped pack of cookies on the table and left, mumbling about a lack of trust.

Keeping her head down, Shara moved along the sidewalk to the house beside hers, and slipped the mail into her neighbor's mailbox. So far so good. Then she headed to Mrs. Cavanaugh's house. As she reached the chain link fence on the side of the house,

Bumblebee and Brambleweed came charging down the narrow strip of grass that was spotted here and there with shade, yellowed grass, and bare dirt. Shara slipped the dog biscuits through a low opening in the fence. After a few sniffs of the air around them, they accepted the treat and trotted back the way they had come. It's not a good idea to reward pets or people for their bad behavior, she thought. But then neither is illegal sperm removal.

As Shara placed the mail into Mrs. Cavanaugh's box, she heard the lock on the front door turn. For a second, she felt like she'd just looked at Medusa and her blood was turning into stone. *Get a grip. You have a lot to lose if you mess this up.* Shara knew she had no way to repay the thousands of dollars Mrs. Nathan had arranged to have given to her for participating—she'd already spent it to buy her house—and she badly wanted the baby they had promised to her. She turned away from the door and took a step forward. When she heard the door open and Mrs. Cavanaugh say, "Hello, Burt," she waved but did not turn around; she just kept walking. *I may have come across as rude to Mrs. Cavanaugh, but, at least if she was asked, she could say she had seen him.* When Shara was sure Mrs. Cavanaugh could no longer see her, she sprinted to the van, tossed the bag inside, and took off for the post office, hoping there really would be a ride waiting for her.

She never even saw Burt's backpack still sitting in the van.

April 1st, 7:42 p.m.

Burt opened his eyes. For a moment, he didn't know where he was or what was going on, but the grogginess slipped away. *I don't remember coming home. I guess it was a long and stressful day.* He realized his headache was gone, and then noticed the bottle of generic acetaminophen sitting in his lap. He looked up at the clock on the living room wall in his apartment, and could not believe it was seven o'clock already. *Awe, shite. I must have fallen asleep. I'm going to be late for my own party.* He headed for the shower, stripping off his postal uniform as he went, letting each piece lie where it fell, like bird crumbs in a cement jungle. He reached for the shower faucet handle. Without waiting for the water to warm, he stepped in and cleaned his body as fast as he could manage. *Ow. That hurts.* Burt didn't know why, but figured his private parts had simply had enough after twenty years of riding in the postal service's delivery van. His discomfort wasn't, however, going to keep him from his retirement party.

John waved at Burt as he stepped inside O'Malley's. John had been sitting at the bar where he could keep a close eye on the door, and the women coming and going. "Hey, Bro," John said as Burt finally strolled in "Thought you'd found a good woman and decided to blow us off."

"No such luck," Burt said. "Although that would have been a better way to end my twenty years with the good, old, United States Postal Service, rather than with a bunch of beer and four other guys." Burt started whistling "Waterfall," and headed with John to share a table with three other male postal workers.

By midnight, Burt had had more than enough beer and was teetering on drunken exhaustion. "I'm driving home now," he said.

"Drunk off your arse, aren't you?" John said. "Hold on. I'll call an Uber to take you home. But first, come on out to my car. I have something for you."

John unlocked his BMW, reached in, and handed Burt his backpack. "Mandy found it in the van after you came back and rushed off. She asked me to tell you thanks for not taking the keys with you, and asked why you didn't come inside for your scheduled exit interview. I laughed it off for you and said that exit interviews are for, um, jerks who care. So, why didn't you do it? Your exit interview, I mean. It looks pretty strange for you to just disappear like that and leave your backpack behind."

"I honestly can't tell you. The only thing I can think of is that the heat and my headache got the best of me, so I headed home and fell asleep."

"Is that why you were late? Man, it's a good thing you're retiring. You act way too old for your age. And I was so sure it was 'cause you were getting a little physical celebration. Too bad for you. Um, speaking of that, I would drive you home myself, but, well, did you see the brunette that was sitting at the bar two seats over from where I was when you finally got here? I convinced her to hang with me after your party was over, so I'm otherwise occupied. Understand?"

"Sure. I'm exhausted anyway. But I'm not old. I have a plan. By the time I retire for good, I expect to have two or three pensions supporting me. All I have to do now is pick another government job with a separate pension plan that I can qualify for without dedicating my whole life to it. Maybe I'll teach. I've always loved kids."

"Ah. And there it is—the plan you promised to tell me about once you retired from this job. Wish you'd told me sooner. Oh, hey. Here's your ride now. Come on, Burt. I'll tuck you in, give the driver your address, and pre-pay for your safe delivery."

One Year Later

Humming softly as she nursed her newborn, Shara rocked side to side. She still could not believe she had given birth to such a sweet baby boy. "Look at you. You're so cute. And you look just like your daddy. Yes you do. You have his big brown eyes and that funny half-smile of his." Her praise was lost on him, however; he'd already fallen asleep. Shara took him to his crib and placed him on his back. Already swaddled, he needed nothing more than to have the light turned out. She kissed her finger then touched it to his forehead. "Sleep well my little Gillie." As Shara quietly closed the door behind her, she heard her door bell ring. *Must be the new onesies I ordered.*

When Shara opened the door, Burt strolled into the house without an invitation, stopped and turned toward her. He held out to Shara the envelope containing the private investigator's report. "I understand you have something that belongs to the two of us."

Closing the door, Shara looked at Burt. "I . . . um." She didn't know what to say.

"You don't have to explain what happened. I already know that part. My PI is quite charming when he needs to be. He even found your accomplice, Mrs. Nathan, and got the truth from her. He said it wasn't easy, mind you, but he also likes her cookies. He also said that he'd help me with you and a great attorney, if needed. Do I need it, Shara?" Burt watched as Shara's expression went from surprise to fear to tears, silent and dainty. "I only want two things—to know why and to see him. Then maybe we can work something out."

Shara wiped her tears and reached out to take Burt's hand. She shushed him and walked him to Gillie's bedroom then opened the door. When they came back from looking at Gillie, Shara put on a pot of tea and sat with Burt at the table.

"The truth is, I never could bring myself to tell you how I felt about you. Then Mrs. Nathan told me you were leaving the postal service, and well, I had made a promise to my mom when she died—she'd always wanted a grandchild—and well, Mrs. Nathan said I could do something good for someone else and keep my promise to my mom." Shara let out a long breath and lowered her eyes from his face. "I'm so sorry, Burt."

Burt reached across the table and took ahold of Shara's hand. "It took me a while to stop being mad at you, but I finally realized I had something—someone—else to think about besides me... And that it was you who made that possible."

Shara looked up at Burt and saw his warm smile and a sparkle in his eyes. She nodded when he said, "So, shall we see what we can work out?"

The Gifts of

Summer

Growth

Knowledge

Maturity

Summer Picnic

by Joe Scavetti

Let's take a lunch to that shady glen
Beside our favorite bubbling brook;

Sip some wine and share some cheese;
Read aloud from a charming book.

Lie in the grass and watch the clouds,
Thinking of what is and what will be.

Falling asleep, my hand in yours,
We'll dream of places we wish to see.

It's the greatest way to spend a day,
Lost in the present – just you and me
.

Issues of Summer

by Darlinda Hagens

Summers of not so long-ago rest at our feet.
Unbeloved facts. Few are willing,
To admit that our lives do matter,
Discounting a truth that's too chilling.

A summer's hate of ignorance and despair.
Knees kneeled, but no, not in prayer.
The weight of one on the necks of many.
Questioning the reality of the word, fair?

Summers of marches, but losing traction,
Screams for justice ignored yet again.
Nothing's hidden, only unheeded.
Exactness of inferiority chimes in the wind.

A summer of love amid the hell.
Sips of peace and conjubilant joys,
Chased by disgust, but rest finds its place.
The issues of summer, addressing men as boys.

No Trip to Oz

by Eva M. Mahoney

"How many people are dead in the cemetery at the end of Azrael?" Yazmine Hardy inquires of anyone who asks her where she lives. And she bounces around, chomping at the bit, just waiting to tell them the answer.

Finally, she gets her chance and blurts out laughing like it is the funniest thing this ten-year-old ever heard, "All of them!"

Yazmine lives on Azrael Street, a street without an outlet. On the corner of Azrael and Dodge stands a street sign that speaks the truth, "Dead End." Yaz loves the irony. She loves to tell people that at the end of her dead-end street lies a cemetery.

"Isn't that just groovy?" she asks. Yaz roars with laughter, and slaps her thigh, her long, curly red head bouncing so much that her silver wireframe glasses start to slip down her nose. The response to her over-acting either makes one laugh with her or makes one raise an eyebrow, as if to say, this girl is so over-the-top.

But today, Yaz is not laughing. Yaz returns home from visiting her friend Peggy, who lives across Dodge and two houses down. Peggy isn't the easiest friend to get along with. Peggy doesn't like the way Yaz dresses. Peggy hates Yaz's hair. It is red, wild, thick, fuzzy, and just out and out too bushy. Peggy shared with Yaz that she believes God got confused when he created her and put pubic hair on Yaz's head. Yaz can't bring herself to ask where pubic hair grows, but can imagine this is not a compliment. Peggy doesn't like the way Yaz says "Groovy" every time she says something Yaz likes.

"Why do you always say that word?" Peggy crosses her arms and looks down her nose at Yaz. "You a hippy now? That's what hippies say. Ms. Henderson says hippies do drugs, burn their bras, and make a lot of noise. You want to do that?"

"I just like the word." Yaz's voice drops to whispering. "Besides, Mrs. Henderson is not a nice person,"

Peggy cuts her off. "She is too! You are such an oddball!" Peggy repeats these words often.

Yaz's feelings are hurt but she will never give up hope that Peggy will look past all that annoys her and just be friends.

"You are too forgiving," Yaz's mom would say.

"I know, but she's my friend."

"Fairweather friend," her mom would correct her. "She only gives you her time when no one else is around"

Yaz knows it is true, but then again there are times when Peggy is really nice to her. They play a game together or work on a school assignment or just watch The Brady Bunch or The Partridge Family and they laugh. Peggy interacts with such ordinary kindness it is hard for Yaz to leave. But then Peggy gets tired of Yaz and tells her to go home. Or worse yet, Peggy calls April Henderson and tells her to come over, right in front of Yaz, and then tells Yaz to leave.

April Henderson lives in the big black house on the corner. She says her house is gray, but it is a dark shade of gray.

April and Peggy are best friends, even though April is a year younger. April and her parents go to Florida every winter during Christmas break and also during spring break. They leave right after the holiday and almost always, Peggy is invited to come along.

Many times, Peggy will go to the mall with April and Ms. Henderson. Once Yaz stood in the hallway of April's home as she told her mother she wanted to bring Yaz shopping instead, because April and Peggy had had an argument. April didn't want to go to the mall without a friend, so she invited Yaz.

Yaz overheard Mrs. Henderson say, "No, absolutely not."

"Why not, Mom?" April asked.

"You know why. You've seen how that girl dresses. Who dresses her? She has no idea that what she wears is so...so dumb. She clashes with her purple and orange. Even you know purple and orange don't go together. And that hair...so unruly. I can't believe her mother lets her go out looking like she does. No, sorry, April, if Peggy can't come, we'll go without a friend."

April walked slowly to the hall. "She said no, sorry," April told Yaz.

"That's okay. Thanks for trying." Yaz replied softly and drudged home.

"Don't matter anyway," Yaz said aloud. The lump in her throat getting harder and harder to swallow. I will not cry; I will not cry. It's so stupid to cry over Ms. Henderson. Yaz tried to think of something else

And now dismissed by Peggy and called an oddball for the millionth time, Yaz hears her mom in her head, "Fairweather friend. Fairweather friend."

"I don't think I'm anymore odder than Danny Partridge. He has pubic hair on his head, too." And despite herself, Yaz laughs.

She walks up her driveway to get her bike. The desire to cry subsides, but Yaz still feels sad. Her bike leans against her house, under the kitchen window. She sees the window opening. It's the kind that mimics a door and is cranked from inside.

"Hey Yaz," her mom, Thelma, calls from the window.

"Hi mom,"

"Good news honey, your dad says that tomorrow we are all going to the fair! All day."

"For real?" Yaz perks up.

"Yep! For real. I'm going to pack a lunch. Your father can get us in for free, but we'll have to watch the money still. "

"Can I play 'I got it'?"

"Yeah, I'm sure we can play a few games of that. Maybe a ride on the big double Ferris wheel, too."

"You think I can?" Yaz hops around in a circle, so happy to hear this.

"I bet you can. You grew a foot since last year."

"That's so groovy!"

Yaz gets on her banana bike. She loves this bike. She got it for free from her uncle whose stepdaughter, they say, outgrew it. Yaz isn't so sure about that. This stepcousin, Louise, is even younger than Yaz and she still thinks the bike is not small on her. Louise behaves like a spoiled brat, insisting Uncle Bob buys her acceptance since he married Louise's mom so quickly after her dad's death. Well, that's what Yaz's mom says. Yaz doesn't care as long as she somehow can benefit from Uncle Bob's guilt.

Yaz rides down Azrael. The homes, set back a bit from the street, have their own distinctive look, not cookie cutter like those found in a new development. Yaz's home is a light gray with a front porch that has a curved roof, which is held up by several white pillars. The Drummen's home, across the street has a cement porch in the front and another on the side. It is one of the biggest homes on the street. The Drummens live on the first floor and often sit on the side porch. The front porch belongs to Ms. Dale who lives upstairs. There is no other home on Azrael that looks like another.

Large maple trees line the street. Their large limbs and branches form a high tunnel of shade. In the fall, the air is filled with helicopter seeds whirling down from the maple trees.

Yaz happily peddles, reveling in the fact that tomorrow she'll be at the Fair...all day. Her dad works there every year the fair comes to town. He's able to get Yaz and her mom and her little brother, Troy in for free. She loves the fair, the popcorn, the way the midway smells as the sun beats down on the asphalt. Yaz keeps her eyes on the ground because often she finds money that people drop. Last year she found a five-dollar bill. She played a lot of "I Got it!" She was too short for the double Ferris wheel and the Scrambler made her throw up, so "I Got it" was her main focus.

She rides past Mr. Burn's big yellow house; past Mr. Smith's; past Mrs. Lorenzo's home and Mr. Carbeck's. Yasmine knows them all. It seems to her that old people are always nice to her. Much nicer than people her age or her mom's age.

She finds Mr. Carbeck working out in his flower bed, so she turns into his driveway.

"Hi, Mr. Carbeck," Yaz says as she comes to a stop, gets off the bike, puts the kickstand down and walks over to him. He looks up and smiles.

"Oh, hi there, young lady. Out for a ride, are you?"

"Yes, sir." Yaz sits down on the grass near him. "Guess what?" she asks.

"Tell me." Mr. Carbeck is so nice to Yaz.

"I'm going to the fair tomorrow. I can't wait."

"Oh, yeah, you like the fair, do ya?"

"I love the fair. It's so much fun. My favorite game is 'I Got it'."

"Oh, yeah, what's that?"

"It's an easy game. It's like BINGO but you play it with little rubber balls. The announcer will tell you when to throw the ball into this bin that has, I think, twenty squares. The balls fall into a square and if you get five across or up and down or diagonal, you can yell out "I GOT IT!" They come around to be sure you really did and if so, you win a ticket. The more tickets you win, the better the prize. Last year I had enough for either this big stuffed dinosaur or a coffee maker. My mom really wanted the coffee maker, so I got it for her."

"Well, that sounds like an interesting game. And that was nice of you to get your mom the prize. You're a good girl, aren't you?"

"For a while, every time she made coffee, she'd say, 'Thanks for the coffee, Yaz.' She stopped saying it, but it was nice to hear."

"Well, hand me that little shovel, will ya, Yaz?"

"Oh, sure." She gets up and finds the shovel and brings it to him. He takes it from her and uses it to dig out a difficult weed.

"School starting for you, Yaz?" he asks.

"Yeah." She does not sound too excited. "That's the one sad thing about the fair. It means school is around the corner. Ugh."

"What grade you going into?"

"Fourth."

"Still in elementary school, are you?"

"Yep. Hey, Mr. Carbeck, you want to see me do a cartwheel?"

"I don't know, you're not going to hurt yourself, are you?"

"Nope. I'm not very good at it, but I will try." Yaz stands up, raises her hands over her head and turns sideways, and says aloud, "hand" as she put her right hand on the ground, "hand" as her left hand touches the ground, but her feet stay put until she flips over, saying, "foot, foot."

As she lies on the grass, she hears Peggy's voice coming from the street.

"You are such an oddball!" Yaz sits up and sees Peggy and April riding their bikes side by side down Azrael.

She lies back on the ground and waits for them to pass.

"Isn't that Jackson girl your friend?" asks Mr. Carbeck as Yaz sits back down at his flower bed.

"Yeah."

"She's got a funny way of showing it."

"She's just goofing around."

"Oh, I see."

Yaz isn't particularly hurt by the words, but the fact that Peggy is hanging out with April and not her, sends daggers to her heart.

"She says I'm an oddball all the time," Yaz confides.

"Aren't we all in our own little way?" asks Mr. Carbeck.

"I guess."

Yaz says her goodbyes to Mr. Carbeck and gets on her bike to ride towards the cemetery to catch up with Peggy and April. She finds them on their way back up Azrael.

"Hey, Peggy, aren't we all oddballs in our own little way?" Yaz blurts out as soon as she's close enough.

Peggy and April stop and appear to be thinking about this.

"But you're the biggest oddball. Bigger than the sun." Peggy smirks.

"I'm going to the fair tomorrow," Yaz says, hoping to change the subject. "My dad is taking me, Troy, and my mother. All day."

"Big deal," Peggy retorts. "April and I are going too. Ms. Henderson is taking us." Yaz misses the surprise look on April's face.

"Groovy. I'll see you there," Yaz says and rides off, ignoring Peggy's "oddball" comment.

"What's wrong, Yaz," her mother asks as Yaz sets the table for three for dinner.

"Nothing," answers Yaz.

"Well, you aren't your usual groovy self, what's up?"

"Oh, I was just thinking that since Troy is too short, who's going to watch him while you and I go on the Ferris wheel? I don't want to go on it alone."

"Oh, we'll figure something out. Maybe there will be someone else needing a Ferris Wheel companion just like you and you can go on with whoever that is."

Yaz didn't respond. Thelma put her hand on her daughter's shoulder.

"Come on, where's my happy-go-lucky Yaz?" Thelma asks with a smile.

Yaz gives her a half smile. "I'm fine, mom."

Later, Thelma asks Yaz, "You want to sleep in my bed with me until your dad comes home?" Yaz loves this opportunity. They have a king-sized bed, and it fits in the corner of the room so that the breeze comes in from both windows. Yaz loves to raise the sheet up, so it floats in the breeze and then falls on her bare legs and arms. Summer is such a cherished season in western New York. The days are limited but mostly they are so nice...warm but not so hot, cool but not cold.

Charlie always tells people from other states, "You can't beat Western NY summers!" And it's so true. After all the snow and cold of the winter; a season that starts right after Halloween and doesn't end until well past most Easters. Even Memorial Day can be iffy.

Yaz likes to hear the story of how her mom's twin sister, Teresa, got engaged right around the same time. Thelma and Charlie got married in January during a blizzard. Teresa said, "No way, I'm getting married in May." And she did, but it still snowed. Granted, not a blizzard but it was cold.

"Yes mom. I'd like to. I'll change and be right back."

"Good, then we can chat," Thelma adds.

Thelma and Yaz have had many talks this way. Any time Charlie works late or all night, Yaz stays in her parent's bedroom. They talk about school and the neighbors. Most often Thelma shares a story of when she and Teresa were young and the twin-anigans they got into. Yaz loves these stories.

With the windows open in all the rooms on the second floor, all lights out and Troy in his bed, Yaz and Thelma start their slumber party.

Before her mom gets there, Yaz raises the sheets and lets them float down. The air feels slightly cool.

Once her mom crawls under the sheet, she asks, "Did you see Peggy today?"

Yaz resists the urge to say yes. She really doesn't want Thelma to think poorly of Peggy, even though Yaz knows Peggy deserves it.

"Did you?"

"Yes, I saw her," Yaz replies, a little more defensively than she intends.

"Did this visit with her have anything to do with your mood...you're seeming kind of down this evening."

Yaz decides to just dive in. "Am I an oddball or a hippy? Peggy says only hippies say groovy. Ms. Henderson says that hippies do drugs and burn their bras."

"Well, she might be right that some hippies do drugs or burn their bras, but, I bet most don't. Being a hippy is not a bad thing, Yaz. Just like being an oddball isn't a bad thing. It means you're an individual, you're not trying to be like anyone else, just being you.

"Next time Peggy or anyone calls you an oddball, you look them in the eye and say, 'thank you!'"

Thelma can see the white of Yaz's teeth as it shines from the nightlight.

"What do you say to that?" Thelma asks.

"I say, 'Groovy'." Both Thelma and Yaz laugh and hug. They are quiet for a minute.

"Now, what do I do about this pubic hair on my head?"

"What?" Thelma asks, not sure she heard correctly.

"Peggy says I have pubic hair on my head."

"Do you know where pubic hair grows?" Thelma asks.

"I think so. Not that I have any, but it grows, you know, down there."

"Yes, but not on your head. Sure, your hair is a little coarse but trust me, it's not pubic hair."

The wind picks up and a gust comes in through the window.

"Doesn't that breeze feel good, Yaz?" Thelma asks. Just as the word "good" is said, the wind picks up and floods through the bedroom, knocking down perfume bottles and knick-knacks off both bureaus. All at the same time, it pushes Yaz into her mom and they both fall to the floor. Loud booms of cracking tree limbs falling to the ground cover Thelma's screams for Troy. And then a thud vibrates through the room. Yaz cries while Thelma holds her as they sit on the floor next to the bed. And suddenly it's quiet.

"Troy!" Thelma yells. "Yaz, we got to go to Troy." They crawl out of the room to the hall in the dark. They get to Troy's room. Still asleep, he doesn't stir.

"Geez, Troy. How can you still be asleep?" Thelma asks as she tries to wake him. "Come on Troy. We need to go downstairs."

Troy wakes up and hears Yaz crying and begins to cry too. Thelma takes them both by the hand; they lean against the wall as they walk down the dark stairs.

Once they get down to the hall, they see a little light shining in. The wind has blown the door open.

"Is someone there?" asks Thelma.

"Thelma, you guys, okay?" asks a voice on the other side of the light. "It's Martin Jones." They can barely hear him. Branches and twigs break up the stream of light coming in from the other side.

"Oh, Martin, we're okay, but what happened?" Thelma shouts back.

"Looks like some kind of wind circulation, like a small tornado came down this part of Azrael. Power is out in the whole area. You got a tree on your house. You should stay downstairs; in case the tree falls further into the house."

"Oh, my! What should I do?"

"Just stay downstairs and inside. There are power lines down and no telling if they're hot. I'm going to continue my walk down. Light some candles if you have them."

"Okay. Thanks Martin."

"Okay, you two. Let's find some candles and just sit down here until your dad comes home," Thelma tells Yaz. She finds Troy already asleep on the sofa.

"Yaz, stay here with your brother. I'm going to feel my way around to look for some candles." Thelma goes into the kitchen, careful to not stub a toe on something in the darkness. She returns to the living room with three candles and matches. And a candle she lit in the kitchen.

"I hope your father can make it to the house. He should be home soon."

"Mom, what if it comes back?" Yaz asks, her voice trembles.

"Oh sweetheart, tornados don't work that way. Once they go through, they climb back into the sky." Yaz nods, this sounds plausible to a 10-year-old.

"I want my dad," Yaz cries.

"He'll be home soon. I doubt the phone will work. I'm going to go back into the kitchen to see, okay? Stay here with your brother."

Thelma sees Yaz in the candlelight. "Oh, honey, you don't have your glasses. You took them off in my room, right?" Yaz nods.

"You got to be brave, okay Yaz? Stay here. I'm going to go upstairs and find them and see if the phone is working up there. I'll be right back." Thelma scoots Yaz onto the sofa and covers her with an afghan even though it's not cold. "I'll be right back."

Thelma takes one candle and makes her way back through the front hall. She can see now that papers on her desk are scattered about. The portable flagpole that stands in the corner until needed to be put out on the front porch during national holidays has been knocked over. She makes her way past that and up the stairs. In her room, bottles of perfume are on the floor. Charlie's Aqua Velva bottle came off his bureau and landed in the laundry basket filled with clean clothes waiting to be put away. Thelma searches the headboard cupboard for Yaz's glasses. She finds them on the floor. Once retrieved, she turns to go back downstairs but before she does, she scans the ceiling. She sees the crack between the wall and the ceiling. It's about two inches wide.

"Oh my," her free hand cups her mouth. She makes her way to Yaz's room. Papers are scattered and things have been knocked off her dresser, but nothing else looks out of place. She makes her way towards the stairs, stopping to check the phone.

Yaz holds the sleeping Troy. "Here you go sweetie. I found them." She tries to put them on, but Yaz has to adjust the ear thingies to fit properly on her face.

"Better?"

Yaz nods her head. She stops crying but Thelma can see the fear. A quiet Yaz says a lot.

"Sorry, but the phone lines must be down. We just have to wait for your father." Thelma joins Yaz under the afghan and they huddle together as they wait.

Charlie finishes his shift at the fair. He can't wait to get home and to bed. It's been a long day of supervising ticket takers and the general administrative duties at Gate 4. He finds his green Valiant in the parking lot. When he turns his car on, he hears the report on the radio of a circulation, believed to be a small tornado, has knocked out power to parts of Riverside. He's surprised to hear "Riverside" as it's rarely mentioned on the news. It's a small village in the town of Joy. Even still, he's not alarmed. After his 20-minute drive, he finds Dodge riddled by tree branches. He sees the lights of the fire company on Azrael and his heart sinks.

"Hey, Charlie," says TJ McPherson, one of Riverside's volunteer firefighters. "You have to park your car on the side of Dodge here. Your street is full of down trees and power lines. Thelma and the kids are fine, but you have a mess ahead of you."

"What the hell happened?" asks Charlie in disbelief of what he has already been told.

"Not sure, but it appears a tornado went right down your street. Knocked down several trees. I haven't gone down there but that's what I'm told. But like I said, Thelma and the kids are shaken up but they're okay."

Charlie gets out of the car and walks the block, viewing the damage in the emergency lights flashing around him. He dodges broken limbs and makes his way across down power lines, making sure to not touch them.

"Oh my," Charlie says aloud when he sees George Rutkowski's Imperial LeBaron, crushed by an uprooted maple tree. The whole tree landed straight down George's driveway so the entire car from bumper to bumper is smashed. Charlie is happy to see George talking to TJ; glad he wasn't in the car when it happened.

As he walks further, past more debris, he finally sees his house. It's not an entire tree, but the main portion of it rests on the one side of the house. In its path, a large limb took down the front porch roof, knocking out the white pillars that held it up. He carefully makes his way to the back door. It's dark inside, but Charlie can see the flame of candles illuminating around the corner into the living room.

"Thelma!"

"Oh Charlie, we're in the living room."

Charlie feels his way in as the candle lights are so dim. He stops at the one cabinet in the kitchen, under the sink and finds the flashlight.

"I remembered this was here," he says, and he walks further into the house. "So glad you guys are okay," he kisses them all.

"I'm scared, Daddy," cries Yaz.

"I know honey, but it's okay now. The tornado is gone."

"Up to the sky?" asks the awoken Troy.

"Yes, up to the sky." Charlie stands. "I'm going upstairs to see what damage there is."

"The roof is lifted up on one side," says Thelma.

Charlie makes his way upstairs to survey the damage. Once he returns, he finds Troy and Yaz asleep on the sofa and Thelma in the kitchen.

"What do you think, Char?"

"It's hard to see in the dark," he says as he puts his arms around Thelma and hugs her close.

"I'm so glad you guys are okay," he says as he pulls away to kiss her.

"I have to say, that was pretty scary. Seemed like a train was coming through," says Thelma.

"I bet," Charlie pauses, his head reeling. "I'll see if Bob can come out and give me a hand tomorrow. At least to get it covered up before it rains."

"Oh! I just realized, Yaz is so looking forward to the fair."

"We'll make it another day. Let's get some sleep." They lay down on the carpeted floor next to the couch, using pillows from the sofa and another afghan. In no time, Charlie snores while Thelma lays awake listening to each breath he takes, grateful to be hearing them.

Yaz wakes up and sees sunlight coming through the side windows. She gets up and all she sees are trees and leaves out of the front windows.

"It's a jungle out there," she says to Troy. He gets up on Charlie's chair and looks out the window.

"Wow, a real jungle."

Their dad, awake for hours, comes in the side door.

"Dad, is it windy out there?" Yaz asks.

"Hi kids. There's a lot of damage all down our street. Yaz if you go out there, please stay away from the power lines. They might be dead, but they could also be not dead, and you can get electrocuted," he tells them.

"Okay. But is it windy?"

"Now? No, it's very nice. Not a cloud in the sky. Go change your clothes and go out there, but stay away from those power lines."

"I'm not going upstairs. That tree could fall on my head." Yaz starts to cry.

"Oh, honey, it's not going anywhere. It's stuck. Don't be so worried.

Just then Thelma comes down from upstairs

"Yaz...here are some clothes for you to wear. I am guessing you're too scared to go upstairs. "

"Hey, does your mother know you or what?" Charlie interjects.

"Thanks mom."

Yaz changes in the living room. She eats a little cereal and goes out the back door. Just as she steps out, Peggy and April come walking up the driveway, avoiding the down lines and scattered branches.

"Hey Yaz," says Peggy.

"Yeah, hi Yaz," echoes April.

"Hi." Yaz isn't sure what to make of this.

"You want to walk down Azrael with us. Check out the damage," Peggy offers.

"Sure. Did a tree fall on your houses?" Yaz asks.

"No, it missed us, but it did knock down our fence."

"Yeah, and our garbage cans are missing," adds April.

They walk down Azrael dodging limbs. They see a big, uprooted maple on Mr. Burns' house. Two doors down Mrs. Lorenz's lilac bush appears to be sucked out of the ground. Another large maple leans against Mrs. Tamraz's house. Further down, the Davis's camper rolled across their lawn like a tumbleweed and smashed into a newly constructed addition to their house.

The destruction of the wind amazes the girls. "I hate the wind," Yaz cries out. "I just hate it!"

"Yeah, it's pretty scary. You should stay at my house tonight, Yaz. At least until they get that tree off your house," Peggy says.

Yaz dries her tears and looks at Peggy but can't think of what to say.

They all survey the area.

"Whoever doesn't have a tree on their house is an oddball." Peggy tells Yaz. It takes a second for that to sink in. Yaz smiles.

"Go ahead, Yaz, say it. I know you're dying to."

April, Peggy and Yaz shout out at the same time, "Groovy!"

Summer at the Castle

by Carla Guthrie

After the disastrous week at the beach the previous year, mom opted, or rather followed her older sister's counsel, in favor of day camp in town. And so it was that, for the next two weeks, I was going to spend most waking hours at the Castle. In spite of the fear of the unknown, the thought sparked excitement as I imagined a turreted fortress, bulwarks included, with thick brown stone walls, an immense courtyard with a well in the middle and all the medieval clichés that my young mind could conjure.

My mother and I walked away from the sun that was barely peeking over the hilly horizon, and treaded the quiet streets of our neighborhood, enveloped by the dewy air. The flashing orange eye of traffic lights pierced the haze, signaling the ungodly hour at which I was to awaken for the duration of camp. I had no notion of time, its passing or any of its attributes, but I still hoped I wouldn't have to do that for very long, I never was an early riser.

We reached the bus stop where an assortment of excited girls and boys were running up and down the sidewalk, screaming and generally ignoring their mothers who, between a piece of gossip and a word of advice they exchanged with each other, scolded them in an attempt to keep them from straying into the street. I didn't know any of them and, to this day, I don't remember any of the faces or names, except J.P.

The bus approached, huffed to a stop, and we piled in. It was an ordinary orange city bus, with creamy-tan hard plastic seats, metal poles to hang on to, and dangling rubber covered loops that none of us could reach. During the ride, I listened to the chatter among the kids, who seemed to know each other, and I gathered they were veterans of city summer camps. They talked of things I knew nothing about and sang popular songs that were obscure to me, an only child of older parents who owned an ancient radio they never turned on, except for the local news. I still have that radio, by the way, lemon yellow with a round wire antenna that folds in the back.

We bumped along the road toward the country, leaving the tall apartment buildings behind. Two-story houses with their small front yards, encased by sectioned metal fencing of browns, greens, grays, and the occasional orange primer, floated by as my thoughts turned to the Castle. I'd never seen it. I'd never even heard of it. It seemed so far away, as I suppose any trip toward an unknown destination feels, the distance magnified by my immature concept of time and space. My sense of anticipation increased as the hills failed to come into view, obscured by the terra-cotta roofs. Impatience kept me glued to the bus window while the other children talked about cartoons, sang more songs, and competed on who was the "coolest". I watched for any sign of a crenellated wall. The bus stopped, waiting for its turn to round a corner onto a road toward the hills. I counted the cars streaming in the opposite direction, they seemed to never end.

We finally turned, and there it stood, not quite at the top of the hill, behind an iron gate, rising above the full silvery heads of the olive trees. It was tall, white with a flat top mounted by finial shaped ornamental terracotta topiaries, a gray stone banister and a stucco wall. The bus proceeded to the back entrance to deposit its load of over excited children. The swarm of bare legs, flapping sandals down the steps, was soon tamed, at least temporarily, and lined up by the camp counselors. I don't remember anything they told us about the rules or the program. After all, it was a long time ago. Most likely, though, my attention was absorbed by the unexpected appearance of the Castle. Why did they call it a castle if it didn't look like a castle? It was my rudimentary way of questioning the conventions of language. Words meant something, right?

We stood in the yard, most of us played with the round pebbles, crunching them under our feet or crouching to sift them through our fingers. The camp counselors had their work cut out for them, herding that little rabble.

Each following morning, it became increasingly difficult for me to rise, and since time cannot be manufactured, my mother compressed it by walking faster and yanking me along harder. My aunt came to the rescue again. She worked for the city, and through her network of acquaintances, she somehow arranged for me to catch the bus at a spot closer to my house. Very close indeed, for we lived a street over from the bus depot, so, for the remaining days of camp, I barely had time to wipe sleep from my eyes by the time I was climbing aboard the orange bus, just me and the driver. It raised the curiosity of the other children to find me on the bus by the time it reached the official stop. Somehow, I had inadvertently broken a sort of hierarchy and I felt their irritation keenly. I secretly enjoyed it, for once I could be more of something than they were.

The days passed at the rhythm of cicadas whirring their deafening cacophony. I spent most days in my swimsuit, standing with the others, stamping on the gravel and jumping rigidly up and down in anticipation of the stream of water hitting my skin. Every hair on my body was raised as the counselors leveled the hose at us in the heat of the afternoon. Water games they called it. We squealed and giggled and ran in place, splashing in the puddles.

As I mentioned, I don't remember the other kids, except for one. He was a special needs child, gangly and erratic in his movements. I wasn't afraid, but he gave me a sense of unpredictability, which made me nervous. With J.P. you never knew what would happen, he could be the gentlest boy one minute and fly into a fear-driven rage at the smallest stimulation the next. On a particular day, I watched the counselors haul him off behind the castle, then I heard some screaming and noise. Curiosity got the best of me, and I inched my way along the wall. Peeking around the corner, I saw J.P. in the fountain's trough, stark naked, getting hosed down. I remember his bewildered, almost pleading eyes, at his feet lay his soiled underwear. The counselors yelled at me to leave, to cover his shame I suppose, or to keep me from seeing a naked boy, maybe both. I scampered off to rejoin the group of kids in the front yard. Although he made me uneasy with his flying arms and noises, my heart was forever imprinted with a sense of compassion for him.

When the heat was stifling, they would usher us into a large room and seat us on each side of the long tables set for our meals: lunch at noon, snack at 4:00, and crafts in between, before they loaded us up on the bus at 5:00 to send us back. The only food I remember was a ham and cheese sandwich, which for me was a novelty. Mom always cooked our meals, and they were definitely more elaborate than just two pieces of bread with one slice of ham and one of Swiss cheese. I had never eaten that before and it made an impression on me. Snacks at home were rich in flavor and variety. They ranged from tomato rubbed bread topped with olive oil and salt to wine-soaked bread with a small mound of sugar over it. Still, I remember the ham and cheese sandwich, not the flavor, just its pale appearance and boring simplicity. Certainly, it was a choice dictated by expediency.

Variety has always been the spice of life that has driven man's mind to be creative with time and resources. One morning, the kind that sticks damp to your skin, they paired us up facing the gate: we were going on a hike through the hills. I am not sure if it was part of the program or if the counselors, drowning in the exuberance of a horde of small children, had raised the white flag and decided that the only way to quench our energy was to get us as tired as possible. Two by two, we walked through the gate, dragging our feet on the gravel. The haze settled on our skin cooling us off and imparting a chill that felt odd on a summer day. I wish I had relished it, because soon enough the sun dissipated any sign of moisture and pricked our bodies with its rays. The asphalt emanated heat waves that rose to bake our feet and legs, bringing the unexpected gift of a strange mirage that made the road look wobbly and shimmering. We chatted and walked, sipping water, lukewarm by now, out of the canteens our mothers had filled for the day.

Suddenly, a scream pierced the hum of our conversations. The kids in the front put on the brakes and the rest of us in the rear guard piled right into them, dispersing to the sides with curiosity. One of the counselors had been bitten by a snake while walking in the grass on the side of the road. The image of hands squeezing his hairy calf around the two holes is framed in my mind. Then a rush of tall people, long hair, a rucksack that produced the kit with the antidote, a syringe, a needle and the gasping and murmuring of our voices as the unfortunate young man offered his leg for the injection.

With the chaos of the incident over, we walked on and, after rounding a bend out of the clump of olive trees that lined the road, I spied in the distance tables spread with snacks and drinks on the lawn in front of an old building. Sweaty and hot, with little energy left, I welcomed that sight. It was afternoon, and I perked up at the thought of refreshment in any form, even bland ham and cheese sandwiches. It was not to be, or at least not yet.

The camp counselors were the keepers of everything, including gauging the level of bladder control in their charges. They divided us into small groups and guided us toward the door of an establishment with an ominous name: The Devil's Tavern. Stuff of legends, no doubt, but I was an impressionable seven-year-old and felt chills reading the sign over the door. I remember shuffling my feet, hesitant to enter the dark, cool vestibule of the tavern.

I froze with fright as I came face to face with the statue of the devil himself, wrapped in his red cloak, complete with horns and pointy tail, grinning maliciously as if he could have reached out and grabbed me. I pushed forward against the other kids trying to get away from that presence that raised every single hair of my body in alarm. I was glad that after the potty break we were taken back outside to partake of the array of sandwiches and rest our exhausted limbs. Once nourished, the bus came by to pick us up to return us to our mothers.

There were reasons beyond my comprehension why the Castle was not a historical attraction like the one in town, which, by the way, was a respectable castle in brown stone, with a tower, portcullis, arrow slits, and crenellated battlements, the true definition of a castle, out of the pages of books that sent my imagination galloping. The Castle, however, had been an insane asylum until four years earlier. It had remained vacant until the city needed a location to hold summer camps. It was a dingy environment and years of neglect had peeled the plaster in patches revealing the gray wall underneath. The faded paint smudged through the years by the hands of tormented souls, lent an atmosphere of despair to the place, while the chipped shutters, with hinges rusted in place, trapped the grief of its past inhabitants like a prisoner. Sadness exuded from the darkness of the rooms, floating about in the stale air.

Had I been told of its past glories, the magnificent castle, even in its ruined state, could have brought a positive breeze in my destabilized young life, shaken by the specter of domestic terrorism, cadenced by daily news reports of death and violence. However, instead of distracting us with the splendor of ages past, the counselors decided to share with us the most recent use of that place, casting a sinister shadow over my impressionable mind. Under the guise of teaching us the history of the place, another stratagem to keep us occupied, I suppose, they escorted us to a small building shaded by a massive fig tree on one side of the yard. They told lugubrious stories and, to make a point - or spook us out - they showed us the "torture" chamber. Upon entering it, I immediately felt uneasy, as we spread out in the skinny room, fanning around a green vinyl examination table. If one were to lie down on it, the wrists would line up with leather straps. Since sheltering children from traumatic experiences seems to not have been a concept in those times, one of the counselors went on to explain to us its barbaric use. My vivid imagination brought forth the figure of a man lying on the bed with his arms tied down and held tight by the leather straps, a rubber block between the teeth, and his back arched as electricity coursed through his body. The anxiety is still etched in my mind.

Years have passed in their cycle, careless of humanity's efforts to slow time down. We tie a thread to events, wishing to never forget in the endeavor to impede its march forward. Some of those threads snap and we are left with a web of memories that does not resemble in any shape or form the actual experiences we lived. Snippets of that summer have accompanied me through life and when I need a palliative to soothe the pain of a struggle, I recall those days and bask in the bright sunshine and puddles I choose to remember. As minuscule as they appear after so long, I also face again the fears that gripped me when I stood in the electroshock room with its two-toned walls, sky blue on the bottom and white on the top, bare patches exposing the mortar underneath. Though faint in my memory now, I imagine again the screams of the patients strapped to the table by leather belts, still supple and dark brown with dirt from the struggling arms that resisted the torture. It seems to hurt me less now, and I am not sure if it's the temporal distance or the fact that somehow my mind has processed the horror, or simply that my heart has been dulled by the intervening and increasingly painful events in my life.

In a strange turn of events, time circled back and handed me the opportunity to revisit the past. The local tourist board started offering tours of the Castle in the summer. After many years and money spent on its restoration, it now houses a school for magistrates. Some would say it has gone back to its former use, but that's satire for another day. So, on a summer morning decades removed, I insisted we join the tour. I was able to secure a spot and thought of the darkened rooms I frequented that summer long ago. The Castle appeared in my mind as it was then, as if somehow the passage of time had forgotten to bring it along. We boarded the bus that would take us there. Funny, the same orange bus with plastic seats, only now I could reach the gray rubber loops to hold on at the curves. And hold on I did, as bus drivers apparently keep to tradition as well.

The houses were the same along the street and as we turned onto the road that stretched upwards, I saw it gleam brightly in the sunshine. As we got closer, the gate revealed its age with rusty spots and the remaining paint sun bleached. The path beyond it was overgrown with grass among the olive trees. No children to scurry around and stamp it down, I suspect. The bus wound around and passed through the back gate. The fountain with its lichen and moss mottled concrete was no longer there, a sidewalk had taken its place. The driver parked on the gravel, raising a cloud of dust. As we got off, I spotted the electroshock building, it had been repainted and the closed door sported a fresh glossy coat. I felt a small pang as curiosity surfaced, and the desire to complete that circle, to feel those fears again, was like pressing lightly on an old wound to see if it still hurt. We were directed to the front of the Castle as the tour was about to start, I looked back at the obscured windows and imagined that now that room probably housed garden tools.

At the foot of the stairs that climbed to the main entrance, we met our tour guide, a man about my age with black hair and blue eyes, who smiled at us as he introduced himself. I shouldn't have been surprised since it is a small town, but behind that grin stood an old friend from my tween years. Suddenly, I was catapulted to my adolescence, sitting on a bench between our apartment buildings, talking to a little boy who happened to go to school with my cousin. Now in his late thirties and I in my early forties, the age gap between us seemed to disappear as time zoomed out from that distant place. As an accomplished art history teacher, he accompanied us up the stairway, and into the atrium. Warm sunshine pervaded the enormous space, airy, tall and grandiose. Freshly painted walls bounced the light back to us in swaths through the grills of the windows. He regaled us with the history that spawned from within those walls.

Anecdotes of the life and times of the Medici family and their entourage fell into place like tesserae to form a picture of history. Our steps echoed in the countless rooms as we listened to the tidbits of knowledge, rich and yet sparse as to what the cadence of days might have been like centuries before. History is like that, dates and salient events top the bulk of a life made of lazy walks in the garden, opulent dinners, spats between spouses and going to the bathroom. Nothing makes you real and human like going to the bathroom. Still, the turbid stories of intrigue and murder lay behind the veil of the ages, they might as well have been etched on celluloid, and as real as I may have cerebrally perceived them, they remained tucked away in a time I did not live nor experience. The dichotomy of real and ethereal spilled over memory and present. The reel I lived as a seven-year-old is reduced to snapshots, fading at the edges, disconnected and impalpable.

Juxtaposed memories of now and then, two facets of the same place, seem to compete to lay claim to reality. However, the new memory can't replace the old one in my heart, the splendor of the restored hunting villa that hosted men and women who shaped history will not supplant the torture chamber and the dining hall, with their damp decrepit walls, and the feelings evoked by new plaster and paint, clean and bright, cannot suppress the emotions I experienced in the past.

Two summers, decades apart, have intersected and enriched my memories, two realities now coexist and inform who I am and will be henceforth. We don't erase the past, we build with it, season by season.

An Unexpected Summer Breeze

by Darlinda Hagens

~1~

A cool, fat, wet raindrop hits my hand as I wave goodbye to Leo Tatum, my martial arts instructor. He offers defense classes in a renovated historical building on the outskirts of Honeyville, Oklahoma, the bustling college town where I live. Since ninth grade, Leo has been a confidence-building force who tried teaching me to stand up for myself. Seven years later, I still run from confrontation.

My steel gray compact car eats up the miles, breezing by coreopsis flowers blooming on the side of the road. I glance right. Just glimpsing the top of the old county bridge sends a shiver down my spine. Since voters believed their tax dollars showed more profit elsewhere, they left the passageway crossing the river to decay. Rumormongers in town love to circulate tales about bodies found in the area.

Several miles zoom past, and I seek the tall wooden cross, topping the white church where I fellowship. Well, when my work schedule allows. Hopefully, after today, Momma can stop complaining about me not attending Sunday services.

Seeing the time on the clock above my car radio, I press harder on the gas pedal. A quick right, and I take a shortcut through Honeyville University where this fall, I will start my junior year. Proud, stately buildings dot the landscape. Pulling onto the road before the hospital where Momma works as a nurse, I shoot on by. Three minutes later, I turn into a parking space at my job and sit staring at the store's sign. Campbell's All Things Healthy.

I slap the steering wheel and get out. "It's the first day of summer, and it's time things change." Lightning crackles, followed by booming thunder. My fear ramps up like it did when I was eight years old, watching a documentary about tornados in Oklahoma without my parents' permission. Huge, whirling, dark clouds plowed a path for miles, tossing houses, cars, and trees like toothpicks. From that day forth, at the first drop of rain, I think of places to seek shelter. Quickening my steps, I dash through the sliding doors.

In the warehouse-size building, I go straight to the bathroom. Long French braids hang over my shoulders as I lean closer to the mirror. Wide brown eyes stare back, and I say, "I, Bianca Blake, will stand up for myself. And I will march into Winston's office and demand he gives me the full-time position with weekends off." Fluorescent lights bounce off my rich complexion as I give myself a thumbs up, tug my work vest over my skinny jeans, and turn on the heels of my new purple Nike tennis shoes. It took me two months to save up for these beauties because of working part time.

Why does finding my way seem so hard? My shoulders slump when I think of roaming HU's campus, majoring in criminal law, knowing with my introverted personality it may never pay off. Still, I want to follow in Daddy's footsteps. Or the path he would have carved out if —

A ripping clash sounds again. The roof seems to shake. I wait for the bathroom's ceiling tiles to fall. Nothing more happens. I exhale a thankful prayer and proceed to the door. Why can't spring just relent to summer without a storm?

Proverbs 23:7, a scripture Momma loves to quote, comes to mind. 'For as he thinks in his heart, so is he.'

Then she adds, 'God may allow twenty-one-year-olds extra time to grasp the big confusing world but at some point, you will need to get it together.'

Wearing my game face, I trek the narrow hallway. The natural stone flooring holds six metal racks of whole-grain wheat bread. I slip past them and arrive at the half glass, half steel office door.

The owner, Winston Campbell, sits behind his small wooden desk in an old leather chair that squeaks with each of his movements. His bald head and muscular build make him look like the guy in a detective series, who my mother swoons over, name LL Cool J.

Mr. Campbell drags his pointer finger down a spreadsheet. His other hand taps numbers into an old 10-key machine. I knock, hoping I do not mess up his count.

His head jerks up, and he rolls his eyes. "Come on in."

"Mr. Campbell —"

"By now, we should be on a first-name basis, Bianca."

"Okay." I square my shoulders. "Winston, I have been here the longest. I've worked this job since the summer before my junior year of high school. Here it is, the summer before my junior year of college —"

"And yet, you're still my youngest employee."

"But that shouldn't matter."

He rubs his bald head. "My other employees have families."

"I have bills and —"

"But you live with your mother, and you're going to college. This place isn't permanent for you."

"How do you know that?"

"Just look at you. You're young, beautiful, and you have your whole life ahead of you." He stands. "Now, don't get me wrong, I want to promote you. You're a reliable, hard worker. I, as a business owner, need people like you, but you're on your way out the door."

With my lips pursed, I give him a sturdy stare. I like Winston. He reminds me of my dad.

He sits back in his seat. "I want you to continue working here, but you deserve better. You should see the world. Meet a handsome man, get married, and have babies."

Hello, this is not 1950. "I have college tuition. A car payment. Car insurance. And I pay half the utilities at home." I lift my foot so he can see my tennis shoes. "Do you know how long I had to save to get these?"

"What if I let you close the store on Saturdays and Sundays? That will give you more hours."

"The main reason I want the promotion is to have weekends off. My mother is already complaining that I can't get up on Sunday mornings for church service. How am I supposed to find that handsome boyfriend if I close every weekend?"

"Bianca, hang in there. Things are bound to change."

"That's what I want. Change. I need a change, Winston."

"Trust me. You'll look back on this job and wonder why you stayed so long."

"Bills. That'll be my answer."

"You're too young to worry so much."

My shoulders slump. I hate confrontation. "If you say so."

"You're still closing the store with Barker tonight, right?"

A long sigh blows past my lips. Mr. Barker, undoubtably, needs the help. Lately, he has complained about hip pain. "Yes, I am."

I leave the office in no better condition than when I went in. Nothing ever changes.

Mr. Barker stands at the tall racks loaded with loaves of bread. Bent forward, one hand massages his back. He wears the classic look of a grandfather. Gray hair, weathered skin, and a smile that puts a heart at ease.

I stop beside him. "Hey, I'm closing with you tonight." I step closer and pat his hand, gripping the rack. "How are you doing? Your hip still giving you trouble?"

"When I was young like you, I would've jumped over these bread holders." He pats the metal rack. "But time always catches up with you." He sighs. "Don't worry about me, little lady. We'll close and I'll go home and put my feet up."

I squeeze his hand. "I can close by myself if you need to leave."

"No. I'm fine." He grabs a few loaves and hobbles in the direction of the bread aisle.

I walk to the cash register with the bold number three high on a pole. After logging in my digital employee's code, I flip on the light. "May I help the next customer?" Person after person comes through my line. I keep my head down, hoping no one sees my heavy heart full of disappointment.

~2~

I glance out the large store windows and compare the falling rain to my life. Nothing ever turns out the way I want. After my father, Benjamin Blake, passed away during my high-school freshman year, I strove to help my mother keep our heads above water. She works the overnight shift, mainly because she misses her husband. Some seven years later, during her weekends off, she continues to sleep on the couch.

Neither of us ever got past Daddy's sudden death. I will never forget the knock on the door or the look in the eyes of his partner, Davis Sims, as he described what happened.

Goodness, I miss my daddy's big laugh. It sounded as deep as Santa Claus's. Roaring up straight from his gut, vibrating his body with a contagious effect. I could never stop myself from laughing whenever he did, whether or not I found his jokes funny.

"Hey, beautiful, I don't mind standing here looking at you, but my practice starts in twenty minutes and Coach is strict about timeliness."

I look up until I reach the most perfect pair of brown eyes. This guy defines the words tall, mysterious, and good-looking. Mercy, he's fine!

My breath hitches in my chest. I cover the gasp with a cough and drag the container of blueberries over the scanner. "So-sorry for your wait."

"No need to apologize. You must have some serious stuff on your mind."

"Not that serious. You play basketball?"

"Something like that."

"For HU?" Not that I ever go to any of the games. My days consist of home, work, school, and church.

He nods. "Doing summer drills. And I'm showing my young brother the ropes. He thinks he can keep pace with me." He leans to one side, showing off his swag, brushing invisible lint from his shoulder.

I giggle and fold my arms. "Oh, you got it like that?"

"Yah huh." He laughs. "Jokes aside, my grandfather lives in Honeyville. He talked about HU so much that I thought I should check it out. I liked the sports program. The rest is, as they say …. Plus, I've enrolled in a few summer classes."

"Just to outdo your brother?"

A frown pinches his perfect brows. "No. I'm heading for the NBA. I want him to come too."

"You aren't from Oklahoma, are you?"

"Boston."

"I could tell from your accent. But yours has more of a Caribbean flavor."

"I'm working on my Okie twang."

He slides his credit card into the machine.

I pass him his receipt. "How tall are you?"

"Six-eleven." He stares at my name tag. "And you, Bianca?"

"Five-five-ish?"

He offers his hand. "Eli James. Nice to meet you, your shortness."

A smile overtakes my face. "Bianca Blake, your tallness."

"Since I know where you work, maybe I'll see you around."

I wave when he glances back before exiting the sliding doors.

My lips remain tilted up. I cannot get the smile off my face. Your shortness. I check out the next customers in a haze.

"Ahem."

I blink to focus. Even amid her beauty, I cannot stop a frown. Emmalyn Bridges. Tall, dark-skinned, almond-shaped eyes, and bow-curved lips make her look exotic. I heard she moved to New York after our high school graduation to model with some high-end fashion designers. Why's she back?

I scan her vegan cookies. "When did you get into town?"

She quirks a finely arched brow. "Did you miss me?"

After the way you bullied me in high school? No! "Just asking a friendly question."

"I can't believe you still work here." She wrinkles her nose as if smelling something disgusting. "But, again, you were always loyal." Rubbing her palms together, she asks, "How's Terrence King? I heard he created a computer app or something and made millions."

"He's still the same."

"I may pay him a visit."

My body tenses and I give her a stony stare. After years of calling him bubble eyes and Bi-focal Buster, now you want to get to know him?

She chuckles. "Calm down. I'm not going to steal your best friend." Leaning forward, she whispers as if sharing top-secret information, "Don't get your hopes up over Eli. He looks like a movie star and talks like a champ, but if you are smart, you'll discount most of his words. He doesn't hold up his end of the deal." She hands me a twenty-dollar bill.

Don't get my hopes up? The man and I just met. "I think you're reading too much into nothing." After counting her change, I ask, "Is he your boyfriend?"

She scoffs. "Read between the lines, Bianca." Dropping her purchase and receipt into an oversize purse, she pulls out an umbrella and sashays away.

Absorbed by Emmalyn's words, I do not even recall my next two customers.

"Hey, goddaughter."

I look up, and my hand covers my heart. "Uncle Davis!" Calling this clean-cut professional man, godfather never felt right, but, for some reason, uncle stuck.

He tilts his head. "How are you?"

"Not bad. It's been a long day, but it's about over now."

"How's Ella? I should visit you and your mother more."

"She's fine, too. Still working all night and sleeping all day."

He stares straight through me. Sadness weighs down his features. And I know without asking what fills his mind. My father's murder. Uncle Davis said robbers ambushed them as they approached a suspect's house, serving a warrant. Daddy, shot point-blank in the chest, never knew what happened.

Uncle Davis shakes his head, and before my eyes, his face transforms into a mega-watt smile. Recently, he threw his hat into the election pot, running for mayor. His friendly manner alone would get my vote. "Tell your mother I asked about her."

I nod and scan his veggie juice.

He hands me a fifty-dollar bill and grabs the drink. "Keep the change."

"No. I can't —"

He jogs out the door.

~3~

Fierce lightning, rolling thunder, and curtains of rain vibrate the skies. A shiver races up my spine. The rumbles sound louder than earlier.

At nine o'clock PM, Mr. Barker, dragging his left leg, locks the automatic doors. He stands around, letting people out and making sure no one else comes in.

After the last customer leaves, I tally up and take the cash drawer to Winston, along with the other employees. Everyone leaves but me and Mr. Barker. We start our janitorial duties: sweeping aisles, emptying trash cans, and aligning items on the shelves, making sure all the labels face forward.

Rounding the corner, I find Mr. Barker sitting on several milk crates, rubbing his back. "I'm not any use to you tonight, Bianca. I've avoided hip surgery. But going under the knife surely couldn't hurt any more than this." He stretches out a long leg and groans.

"Go home. I'm almost finished. I can lock up."

"Little lady, I can't leave you here alone. Anything could happen."

If something happened, in his condition, he could not even run for help, let alone stand up and box a thief.

A blaze of lightning claps over the building. I look up, expecting the roof to cave in. "I doubt if anyone will come out in this weather for some healthy stuff. Winston took the money to the bank. He's the one you should worry about." I take Mr. Barker's arm and help him to his feet. "I just need to empty the trash and I'll be out of here."

"Well, alright."

I walk him to the front door. "I'll see you tomorrow night."

"Call me when you get home, so I can rest tonight and not have nightmares of you lying dead on the floor."

"You're worrying about nothing, but okay, I'll call." I stay under the awning as he limps to his compact-size truck. Before he makes it to his vehicle, the downpour increases.

I dash back inside and lock the doors. Standing at the large window, I watch until he pulls out of the parking lot.

After closing, the fluorescent lights automatically dim to half brightness. Now, in this oversize building alone, the walls seem to come to life, swaying and bowing under the power of deafening thunder. Rain, beating the metal roof, causes nervous energy to bounce like a ping-pong ball, hitting every one of my nerves from head to toe. I focus on my tasks, finishing up as fast as possible.

By the time I bag the garbage, the cascading sounds from outside ease up. I go to the back door. The hazy security light on the pole flickers, unsure if it should keep shining or go out. Stepping out into the nearly nonexistent beams begs for a mugger to pop out and whack me over the head.

If Winston wants me to keep working here, he better repair the lights. I look both ways, then hurry toward the dumpster. When I glance down, I frown. Oh, Father on high, my new Nikes!

Tiptoeing around puddles, I sling the trash bag as hard as I can. A sigh of relief blows from me when the bag makes it inside the garbage bin.

A yelp rings out.

I jerk back, expecting a cat to pounce over the sides. Even knowing my shoes become soggier by the second, I shuffle in place, waiting. Nothing happens more than a summer breeze dampening my cheeks.

As I turn to go inside, a squeal sounds. This time it comes from lower down. My sight tracks across the ground, seeking the source. Lightning performs a show, striking several times, leaving explosions in its wake. But the added light helps me spot a black backpack leaning against the base of the dumpster.

Something to the left moves in my peripheral vision. I spin around with my heart in my throat. "Who's there?"

"Waa!"

I turn back toward the dumpster.

Mewls draw my attention to the backpack. I inch closer to the dark bag, still glancing over my shoulder. Someone else is here.

Logic tells me to run back inside. But the sobs will not let me. This could be some weird booby trap. A bomb or anything. Shouldn't I call the police and ask them to send a robot out to check this?

Rain falls harder. I close my eyes and ease the zipper back. Instead of an explosion, a whimpering rises out of the opening. Something soft shoots out and latches onto my pinky finger.

I scream and hurriedly zip the bag closed.

The rainfall pours like the shower in my bathroom when turned on full blast.

I hesitate, then snatch up the backpack and dash into the store. Tremors overtake me. I can barely lock the door. Feeling semi-safe, I slide to the floor, kneeling before the backpack.

Something inside moves the canvas bag as if trying to get out.

My hand covers my mouth. I gulp down another scream. Ooh, Jesus. Help!

With stiff fingers, I grip the silver pull. The slider glides over the zipper's teeth. Inch by inch, I push it across the top and down the side. Then I peek inside the waterlogged bag.

A powerful gasp knocks the air from my lungs. I can hardly stop myself from collapsing on the floor in a dead faint.

A baby!

Dark hair covers a small head. "Gracious God," rolls off my tongue again and again as I reach inside and tug the infant free.

Holding it out with my hands around its chest, the head bobs back. It stares into the dimmed glow as short legs kick.

It's a girl.

She focuses on me. I know this child is too young to make a plea only by using its sight. But I could swear, for just a second, her eyes lit up and her little round face softened.

The baby whimpers.

A sob catches in my throat, and my heart beats with renewed purpose. "Hey, how old are you? An hour? Three, maybe?"

A pink ribbon, tied in a bow, dangles from the end of a shiny yellow lump, extending from the infant's belly button. I cradle her in my arms. She relaxes and her tiny hand grasps my pinky.

As if the baby whispers her name to me, I say, "Grace? Okay, I'll call you, Grace."

I did not realize I owned a grain of motherly instinct, but as I hold this child, something rises from the depth of my soul. It may not be love, but it feels very close to it. I have never wanted to help anyone as much as I want to help Grace.

Who would throw a human being in the trash?

My parents did not drop me off at a dumpster, but I endured many lonely years. Daddy worked until late evenings, and Momma always took the overnight shifts. Obediently, I tiptoed around, not disturbing them as they slept, staying in the house, sitting in the window, watching the neighborhood children play hopscotch, jump rope, and barbie dolls. If not for my best friend, Terrence King, calling to say hi, I would have gone insane.

I wobble to my feet while cradling the newborn, sling the backpack over my shoulder, and head to the front of the store. Grabbing a shopping cart, I place the backpack on the bottom and cover the dampness with my work vest, then I lie the baby on top of it. As I push the child down the aisle, I realize I do not know the first thing about babies.

The infant cries the sweetest little cry. She seems to shiver with her fist clenched. Another sob bubbles up in my throat. First, I grab one of Winston's organic cotton blankets. I open it on the spot and tuck it around the baby. She turns her face into the softness and makes smacking sounds.

Food. She needs food.

I keep a hand on her as I roll to the baby formulas. Goodness, with so many selections, I stand clueless. What if I pick the wrong one? I read several labels and decide on the lactose-sensitive one.

Baby bottles.

I pick up a couple of anti-colic bottles for newborns. Moving to diapers. I choose some plant-based newborn ones and organic wipes.

Winston opened this health store because his son was born with every imaginable allergy. So, everything in his business carries an element of health.

After tearing into the package, I snatch out a diaper and put it on Grace. Goodness, she hates diapers. Amid her kicking and screaming at the top of her lungs, I secure the back to the front with the tape strips. One side hangs low, and the other appears much too high, but I do not redo it. Instead, I quickly swaddle her in the blanket, and she calms down. One-handed, I stash the baby's items in the black backpack, heft it over my shoulder, and take the child alone with me into Winston's office. I leave money in his desk drawer with a note: I made some purchases after closing. Add this to my cash drawer. Thanks.

On the way out of the store, I grab an umbrella from the display. With the store locked up, I bolt into the rain, caring more about keeping the baby dry than ruining my new tennis shoes.

I make it to my car and fumble with the key fob. Again, I jerk around. Something moved in the tall shrubs.

When the lights flash twice, I drop the umbrella, jerk the door latch, throw in the backpack, and slide behind the steering wheel with the baby clutched to my chest. Hurriedly, I hit the lock button. Turning in every direction, I wait for the monster lurking in the bushes to introduce himself. Nothing?

Rain washes my windshield as I lay the baby in the passenger seat and click both of our seatbelts. Not that her restraints matter, it barely touches her.

I speed out of the parking lot with one hand resting on the child's tummy. My wiper blades work as fast as the jitters skipping down my spine.

Three miles in the heavy downpour, and I pull into my driveway. The headlights shine on the forest green artisan-style home I live in. Although I associate this place with a lifetime of aloneness, it also holds a peace that I cannot find anywhere else. As I turn off the ignition, my sight goes to the swing on the wide front porch, then to the symmetrical large front window, offering a view of the neighborhood.

Since Momma works the graveyard shift, I do not worry about facing her. Pulling my cell out of my pocket, I dial my best friend. "Terrence. Can you come over?"

"I love you, Bi, but can't it wait until tomorrow? I'm working on another app. I think I already have a buyer."

"Terrence! I need to show you something. Meet me in the shed."

"I'll be right there." His voice drops, and I wonder if I imagined the passionate tone.

I end the call and dial Mr. Barker. "I'm home."

"Good. Now I can relax. Sleep well."

"You, too." I shove the phone back into my pocket and glance at the passenger-side seat. I've lost my mind.

The baby whimpers. I ease the bundle into my arms. Clutching her to my heart, I step out of the car. God, what's wrong with me? Why can't I act like a normal person? Anyone else would've called the police.

Slinging the backpack stuff with the purchases over my shoulder, I hurry around to the back of the house, following the stone path leading to Momma's shed. Under the welcome mat, I find the key and step inside.

The scent of lemons freshens the air, telling me Momma recently cleaned her beloved space. I flip on the light. Beneath the warm colors of the décor, stands shiny flooring. A plush loveseat angles in a corner. Under a small window, the polished mahogany table holds a crystal vase filled with wilted flowers. The last bouquet Daddy gave Momma. No one can find the courage to throw it away.

I place the sleeping baby on the couch, the bag on the table, and pace back and forth from wall to wall. What will Terrence say when he gets here? I glance at the infant. How do I explain this to him?

Our friendship began way back in grade school. As bookworms, we made an instant connection. His thick glasses and overbite blended well with my boney legs and introverted personality.

A banging on the door makes me jump. The baby does not like it either. Her whimper expands into a full-blown wail. Unable to decide between answering the knock or soothing the baby, I scoop the little girl up and rush to the door.

Terrence stands in the drizzle that continues to fall. His eyes widen as he stares at the bundle in my arms.

While he fixates on the baby, I study him, noticing things I missed during the years. I must feel like Momma when she asks me, 'when did you grow up?' She still sees me as the eight-year-old wearing laced socks and pigtails. Same with Terrence, I see things I observed, but simultaneously failed to notice.

Like, I knew he now wears contacts, but I cannot for the life of me remember when he stopped wearing those funny-looking pop-bottle lens glasses. Until this moment, whenever I looked at Terrence, in my mind's eye, I always saw him as my nerdy neighbor with the thick bifocals. Tonight, in the dim she-shed light, I see him for the man he has become.

His mouth twists into a nervous smile, and his teeth seem to gleam white as snow. What happened to his braces? How on earth did I miss his perfectly straight teeth? And goodness, he's tall. Not as tall as Eli, but surely over six feet.

Butterflies flutter in my stomach. I gaze at his damp shirt, hugging his bulging biceps and ripped abs. Maybe the baby in my arms makes me see my childhood friend as his true self and not the vision I have carried for so long.

His deep voice snaps me out of my trance. "Are you going to leave me out here all night?"

I scoot behind the door, making room for his entrance.

When he stands inside, the space seems to shrink to less than half of its already small size. "Bianca." He inches closer to me. "Is that a baby?"

I nod. "Grace."

He scoffs. "Who, in their right mind, gave you a baby?"

"You don't have to say it like that."

"Bi, I watched you play with dolls. None of them kept their heads. You were so rough combing their hair, you decapitated each one." He laughs at my frown. "Now, who gave you a baby?"

"I found it."

"What?"

"Someone left her. They zipped her up in that black backpack over there." I jerk my head toward the table while bouncing the baby in my arms.

Terrence strides to the backpack and pours all my purchases on the tabletop. A soggy note falls to the floor. He snatches it up and reads, "I can't take care of her. E." He turns to me. "Who's 'E'?"

"Not me."

He smirks. "How do you know her name is Grace?"

"I didn't, I named her."

Air puffs his cheeks, and he lets out a long, streaming sigh. "This is not a puppy you found on the street."

"I know that, Terrence."

He walks over and peeks inside the blanket. "She's gorgeous. Grace fits her. Where did you find her? Did you call the police? We need to call Ms. Ella. She's a nurse and this child may need medical attention."

I did not think of that, but I will not call my mother. Well, not right now. I do not want to hear one of her lectures. "I'll tell Momma, but later. You know how she gets. Just help me figure things out, Terrence."

"Bi, we may both go to jail for kidnapping if we don't think fast."

The baby cries.

He smooths his large hand over her tiny head. "Have you fed her?"

"No. I don't know about this stuff."

He shakes his head. "Is the key under the same plant on the back porch?"

I nod.

Terrence picks up the baby formula and a bottle. "Wait here."

"How are you so knowledgeable about babies?"

He arches a thick brow. "I'm the oldest of four, remember?" He eases the shed's door close.

"Shh, baby. My best friend knows what to do." Pacing back and forth, I hate I acted on instinct. I should have called the police the second I pulled the child from the backpack. Momma always says, I never stop to think before acting. I just proved her right. I pick up the note: *I can't take care of her. E.*

The handwriting could belong to anyone. I consider all the people I know with the initial 'E'. Even my mother's name starts with an 'E'. Today I spoke to two people in the store with names beginning with 'E'.

I sit down, rocking the dozing baby. What if this beautiful child belongs to one of them? Emmalyn looked too elegant, too pampered, and too educated to leave a child near a dumpster. I doubt if she ever even approached a dumpster. Eli, tall, handsome, with so much swag. I cannot picture him doing something so heinous.

Terrence returns, hands me a warm bottle of milk, and sits beside me. Grace greedily accepts the odd shape nipple. We watch her eat.

I can barely pull my eyes from the newborn to look at my friend. "You're right. I should've notified the police first thing. I think I wanted Grace to feel loved before handing her off to strangers."

"Bi, you've always had a big heart. That's what I love most about you."

"Terrence, my impulsive move could destroy both of us."

"Call your godfather."

I release a long sigh. "I pray he does not tell Momma."

This cute little face cradled under my heart is an outcast. Since Daddy's passing, I have felt like one, too. I cannot blame my mother, she's wonderful. If only I could find my footing. Today, I could not even persuade Winston to give me a promotion after all the years I worked at the health food store. No pity parties. Ugh!

The baby finishes the bottle, and Terrence eases the infant out of my arms. He looks at the crooked diaper and the pink bow dangling from her belly button.

"Judging from her umbilical cord, she's only a day no more than two days old."

He places the baby over his shoulder and pats her back. "We got to burp her."

"What?"

"Get the air out of her tummy?"

Something else I did not know. Fate did not choose well for you tonight, little one. Soon she releases several soft burps.

I stand and pull my cell from my pocket, scroll to the number, and put the phone to my ear. "Uncle Davis, I need help."

He listens as I give him the details. Then he asks, "You took the baby from the scene of the crime?"

"Yes. I just kinda reacted."

"Okay. Okay. Let me think."

My sight goes to Terrence. His brows rise, asking silent questions.

"This is what I need you to do." Uncle Davis speaks in a calm voice. "Go back to your job. Meet me at the dumpster with the baby in twenty minutes."

"Go back?"

"Yes. If anybody asks, you never left the scene. Bring the empty backpack and the note with you."

"Okay."

"I'll see you there." He ends the call.

I turn to Terrence, snatch up the baby's crumpled blanket lying beside him, and spread it out on the loveseat. "Uncle Davis wants me to meet him at the dumpster."

My friend nods as he lays the sleeping child on the soft white covering.

I pass Terrence my car keys. "You drive, please?"

He stands. I swaddle the child and cradle her in my arms. A lump the size of an avocado pit sticks in my throat. Tears fill my eyes. What will happen to her? How could any of this happen to someone so innocent?

Terrence wraps me in his arms, careful not to squeeze the precious bundle. "Everything will be alright, Bi. There are good people in this world, and someone will love Grace as much as, or possibly even more than, you love her."

"I know. You're right." I brush moisture from my cheeks.

Terrence goes to the table. "Are we taking this care pack you made for her?"

"Nope. Just the empty backpack, the note, and the baby."

He puts the purchases inside the dark bag, anyway. "I'll throw these in your garbage can as we leave out."

While he holds open the door, I amble outside with Grace pressed to my chest. The muggy summer heat holds dampness left behind by the rain.

He locks the shed, and I follow him to the trash receptacle on the side of the house and watch him drop the items, one by one.

I kiss Grace's little head through the blanket and pray handing her over to Uncle Davis will change her outcome for the better.

It does not take long for us to pull into the store's parking lot. I direct Terrence around the back toward the alley. He parks a short distance from the dumpster and turns off the ignition. Soon, headlights round the corner, heading our way.

"I think that's Uncle Davis."

Terrence runs around the car and opens my door as the black Ford Crown Victoria, which most police detectives drive, pulls behind us.

"Goddaughter." Uncle Davis gets out, staring at the blanket. "Is she in there?"

I peel back a few layers and expose her to the night air.

"Good, Good." As he looks around, I cover up the baby. "Bianca, I need you to trust me on this. This is what's best for everyone. Where's the backpack?"

Terrence hands it to him.

"Now show me where you found it. We're going to stage the scene again."

Both men follow me to the back of the dumpster,

"There." I point.

Uncle Davis places the backpack against it. He turns to me. "Like this?"

"Yes."

"Good. Good." He pulls out his cell and taps a number. "We're ready."

A police vehicle pulls forward with overhead lights flashing. Three news vans follow the patrol car. A white sedan parks behind the last van.

I hug the baby tighter. "Uncle Davis? W-what's going on."

"I thought this would be an opportunity that helps both of us."

The squad car angles across the alleyway, blocking traffic. Names of local television stations show on the side of the vans. A crew of people crawl out with beaming lights, cameras, and microphones.

"Um. What?"

"Since I'm running for mayor, this will boost my recognition for when I run for governor and then the presidency. As well as take the child into custody where she will be safe."

This does not seem right. "You're exploiting a newborn?"

"No, no. We're helping this poor, beautiful child while we help ourselves."

"Ourselves? I don't need help."

"The child does. Now smile for the cameras and let me do the talking."

Uncle Davis deserves an Oscar for his performance. He answers questions directed at me, as I watch, flabbergasted.

A lady wearing a gray pantsuit gets out of the white sedan. Pushing her collar-length blond hair behind her ears, she shoves her way past the anchor people and Uncle Davis. Flashing her ID before my face, she says, "I will take the child now."

Unconsciously, taking a step back, I bump into Terrence. He wraps his arms around me as if shielding both me and Grace. I try to swallow the ache in my throat, but it will not budge. So, I screech out the words, "Where-where are you taking her?"

Crossing her arms, she heaves a sigh. "After a medical examination and paperwork, the child will go to one of our many emergency-foster homes." She holds her hands out.

Not wanting to cause a scene, I gently lay the swaddled baby in her arms. Not an ounce of affection crosses the social worker's face as she pivots on her low heels and marches back the way she came, carrying Grace.

I race after her. Terrence's footsteps thud behind me. I glance around to find news anchors following us.

At her vehicle, the social worker opens the rear door and removes the oversize cotton covering I wrapped around Grace. She shoves it into my hands. Putting the child in a car seat, she tucks the baby in a pink blanket custom-fit for a newborn. I want to reach in and touch Grace one last time. But the social worker's body blocks me out.

"What happens after the emergency-foster home?"

"Long-term care. We leave the legal part of this situation up to the courts." She hits the lock button and slams the door. The slam startles Grace. She wails at the top of her voice. The worker seems to turn a deaf ear to the cries and walks to the driver's side.

I pull on the door latch, although I know it's locked. A sob bubbles up, and tears blur my vision. My hands cover my face, and I join Grace in a heart-wrenching cry. Terrence wraps me in his arms.

"Excuse me, Miss."

While dragging my fingers under my watery eyelids and runny nose, I turn to find a handsome man with dark hair sticking his microphone in my face.

"Tell us the truth, why are you so upset over that baby? Are you the mother?"

"What? No! I'm human. Why aren't you affected by a baby left by a dumpster?"

He moves the microphone to Terrence. "How do you feel about the infant? Are you the father?"

Uncle Davis moves in front of us, redirecting the question back to the crime that was committed while generating publicity for himself.

Terrence takes my hand, and we rush to my car. Before I know it, we're on the road back to my home.

Straightening my slumped shoulders, I sit up tall and wipe away tears. "I need to go by Ms. Eartha's."

"Are you sure? I think you need to go home and pull yourself together."

"I didn't drive by her house after work tonight. You know how she is."

Moments later, Terrence turns into Eartha's driveway. Yet, again, she forgot to close her garage door. The street light shines on the red brick ranch-style home. I lean forward, peeking through the windshield. Her blue Prius is parked inside the dark space. "See, this is the reason I must check on Eartha every night."

Even though Eartha is three times my age, we quickly became friends. Upon meeting her on the day of my father's funeral, she told me she had worked on a few cases with Daddy. Taking my hand that day, she shared her life story. Saying, during her day, few women applied for positions in law enforcement. After retiring, she used her detective credentials and opened her own private investigating business. She said age and bad knees made her close shop. But Eartha encouraged me to follow in my father's footsteps. Years later, when I enrolled in college, I heeded her words and majored in criminal law. Still, I pray I made the right choice.

Terrence stands at my side on Eartha's wide porch, lit by a yellow porch light. I ring the doorbell. It seems like an eternity before she peeks out of her glass-pane door and flashes a big grin. Fumbling with the lock, eventually, she opens the door.

I force myself not to adjust the twisted silver chain around her neck bearing the uniquely designed black diamond 'E'. And mercy, how I want to straighten the wig sitting skewed on her head.

"Sweetie-sweet!" She hugs me.

"Eartha, you left your garage door up again."

"Sweetie-sweet, you sure?" Waving us inside, she says, "Come on in, sweet people. Was that you on the breaking news tonight?" She winks at Terrence. "And I saw you, too, handsome."

Her walking stick taps the hardwood floor as her pink house shoes make swishing sounds. Eartha stands about as round as she is tall. She reminds me of Aunt Bee on the old black-and-white reruns of the Andy Griffith Show my mother loves to watch.

Eartha arrives at her favorite chair, a brown leather recliner, and points for us to sit on the leather couch beside it. "Terrence, go hit that garage door button for me, sweetheart."

As he leaves the room, she leans forward. "How did you end up with the baby?"

"Someone left her by the dumpster behind my job."

"Young people nowadays. And you don't know who?"

I shake my head.

She sits back and steeples her fingers. "I may need to put my P.I. hat back on for this one."

"Please do Eartha." I lean closer to her. "I took the child home. But when I called Uncle Davis, he told me to take her back to where I found her, and he would meet me there. I didn't expect the local news to show up."

"Sims. Your father's partner? Now he's running for mayor." She quirks a brow.

Daddy, Uncle Davis, and Leo Tatum are all law enforcers. Eartha said after my father, she likes Leo the most. So, I doubt if my godfather gets her vote. "Thank goodness Uncle Davis answered most of the questions."

She leans back in her recliner. "Well, that should've put him on the map."

"I'm sure it did."

My cell rings as Terrence walks back in and sits beside me. Uncle Davis's name flashes on my phone.

"Goddaughter. I apologize for the news media. But it worked out for both of us, right?"

"I guess. Do you think I will ever see the baby again?"

"Why don't you come to my office tomorrow? We'll have lunch and discuss your options."

"Okay."

"Good night. I'll see you tomorrow."

I disconnect, slide my phone into my pocket, and stand. "Eartha, it's late. This has been a long day."

"Sweetie-sweet, thanks for checking on me." She grins.

Some days, I think Eartha intentionally leaves her garage door open just so I will stop in and visit with her.

Terrence and I follow her to the front door. She stops and grabs our hands. "Let's pray before you venture back into the big, dark world."

We form a circle and bow our heads. "Lord Jesus," Eartha says, squeezing my hand. "You see things we can't. You know things we don't. And because you are the all-knowing and Almighty protector, we ask you to watch over Sweetie-sweet and her handsome boyfriend, Terrence."

My best friend and I glance at each other. He winks, and I wonder if everyone sees us as a couple, or is it just Eartha's wishful thinking? Sidetracked by my wandering thoughts, I miss most of the prayer but zero in when she mentions baby Grace.

"God, let your love follow that child wherever she goes." Eartha squeezes my hand again. "In Jesus' name, we pray. Amen."

As I hug her good night, I whisper, "Thanks for the prayer."

She kisses my cheek. "I love you, Sweetie-sweet. Drive safe."

When I step aside, Terrence wraps his arms around her shoulders. "Ms. Eartha, be sure to lock up, I may ride with Bi tomorrow to check on you."

"I could stand a good-looking man in my life."

Unable to stop an eye roll, I say, "Ms. Eartha! You're such a flirt."

"You just now figured that out?"

The three of us stroll onto the front porch. Eartha says, "I hate I didn't go by Campbell's health food store today to check on Mr. Barker."

Breathing in the freshness the rain left behind, I walk to the banister. "He left early. His hip was bothering him."

"He just needs me to lay hands on him."

My mouth drops, and I jerk around to find Eartha's eyes sparkling with humor. Laughter charges through me, sounding much like my father's belly laughs. Happiness rises in my heart for the first time since

Grace left my arms. "Ms. Eartha, what am I going to do with you?"

Leaning heavily on her cane, she goes back inside and sticks her head out the door. "Good night sweetie-sweet." She looks at Terrence and winks. "You too, handsome."

After hearing the deadbolt click in place, Terrence and I head for the car. He opens the passenger side door. And I climb in, still giggling. "Terrence, I may have found you a woman."

"She's older than I like. I want someone around your age." He arches a brow.

My smile slides down my face into my shoes, and my heartbeat ramps to triple time. I cannot tell if he made a joke, or if I should take him seriously. But his words sink into the pit of my stomach, awakening butterflies.

Awkwardness descends in the car during the ride home. Tonight, I notice everything about my best friend. The smell of his cologne. The way he leans to the side as he drives. How his long fingers grip the steering wheel. I breathe a thankful sigh when Terrence parks in my driveway.

The stars glow in a partially cloudy sky; the moonlight peeks between the tree's low-hanging branches. Terrence follows me to my front door. "Bi, will I see you tomorrow?"

"I'm having lunch with Uncle Davis, then I go to work. But I'll call you."

He kisses my cheek. "Sweet dreams."

"Night, Terrence."

He bounces down the steps of my porch, heading to his home next door. I go inside. Momma lies on the couch.

She pops up. "The Lord giveth, and taketh away, blessed be the name of the Lord. I saw you on the television while I was in a patient's room. I almost dropped her meds. So, you're a celebrity now?" Momma's deep complexion gleams under the lamplight. Curls hang on her graceful shoulders.

I hasten to her and throw my arms around her neck. "No Ma'am. I'm just someone who tried to help a newborn."

She draws me down beside her on the couch. "I'm just grateful you did nothing silly like bring the child home."

I pick lint balls from her blanket. "That would not have been wise."

Her finger goes under my chin, forcing me to make eye contact.

To her, reading my mind comes easy. "You did, didn't you?"

"Just for a little while. Then Terrence and I called Uncle Davis."

"Bianca."

"Momma, I didn't know what else to do."

"Poor, Terrence. That young man would fly to Mars if he thought it would make you happy." She sighs. "Thank goodness your godfather had everything under control."

"I was grateful he stepped up." I kiss Momma's cheek and stand. "Long day. I'm calling it. Love you, good night."

"Bianca."

I stop in my tracks and slowly turn.

"Proverb 3:27. Withhold not good from them to whom it is due, when it is in the power of thine hand to do it."

Does that mean I did the right thing? "Yes, Ma'am."

I shower, crawl into bed, and dream of me and Terrence caring for Grace.

~4~

Standing before the solid door, I read the gold nameplate. "Davis Sims, Deputy Chief of Police." I knock.

"Come."

When I push open the door, I inhale the scent of freshly brewed coffee. A percolating coffeepot sits on a small table in a corner, surrounded by paper cups, creamers, and sugars.

My godfather sits at his solid mahogany desk dressed in a blue suit and white shirt. Stacks of manila folders lay open around him. He stares at the screen of his desktop computer.

I ease into a leather chair fronting his desk. He holds up a finger, then finishes typing something. I remain silent and relax in the chair.

After my father's death, Uncle Davis climbed the promotion ladder. To top it off, now he is running for mayor. He said the governor of the state stands next in line, and then the presidency. I must admit he dreams big.

In the middle of a decorative wall of plaques and accomplishments hang pictures of Daddy, my godfather, and Leo Tatum. I stroll to the photos. Instead of the stern looks showing on the other men's faces, my father wears a smile. His love for humanity shines in his eyes. An ache pierces my heart, I miss him beyond measure. Never caught, my father's killer runs free. When I majored in criminal law, I hoped to one day have the privilege of bringing the murderer in.

"Hi, Bianca."

I turn to find my martial arts instructor standing in the doorway. Even though he is a devoted detective enforcing the law in the community, Leo's personality does not hold the pizzazz of Uncle Davis's. He behaves more straightforwardly. A get the job done temperament. In my gut, I believe if Leo would have been on duty the awful day my father died, things would have turned out differently.

Sleeves rolled up, showing his muscular forearms, he walks in, glimpses the photos on the wall, then looks at me. "I know you're full of surprises, but I didn't expect to see you on breaking news."

I glance at my godfather, sitting in his high-back, black chair. "I know Uncle Davis told you what happened. It was very unexpected."

"No, he didn't. But it's been a busy morning. Is that why you are here visiting Sims?"

I nod.

Uncle Davis shuffles from behind his desk and stops beside us. "Your father, Leo, and I worked well together. When one took a call, the others followed. Benjamin Blake was a great man. Leo and I will never find another partner as loyal as your dad."

"That's true," Leo says, pulling me into a hug. His big arms squeeze me tight. The side of my face presses into his chest, and I hear the thumps of his heart. Both of my father's partners show affection easily, but Leo's warm embrace reminds me of Daddy's.

He releases me and speaks to Uncle Davis. "Sims. You're holding me up, man. I need your report so I can finish my investigation."

"That's what I'm working on now."

Leo turns to me. "We still need to work on that chokehold. Without waiting for my reply, he leaves the room.

Uncle Davis walks back to his desk. "I hope you don't mind a quick lunch at the burger joint around the corner." He takes a gun out of his drawer and slides it into a holster under his jacket.

Soon, we sit at a window table, talking about everything but the infant I found last night. Finally, I ask. "Do you know where they took Grace?"

"Who?"

"The baby the social worker took."

"Oh, right? Well, the child's whereabouts are confidential. I'm forbidden to give away the location."

I drop my head, but immediately pull myself up straight. "Then what was the purpose of this visit?"

"Mainly, I wanted to see for myself that you're okay." His oversized palm covers my hand on the table. "As soon as we can release that information, you will be the first to know."

I jerk my fingers from his grasp. "I'm not worried about myself. Grace is the one who matters."

"I agree. But you matter to me."

The look of concern in his eyes makes me reach out and take his hand again. "I don't know what I would've done without you last night."

"I'm always here for you, Bianca. Always."

"I know." Pushing my barely touched plate aside, I stand and hug him. "I got to get to work."

~*~

Making my way through the warehouse, I go to Winston's office and knock.

He waves me in. "I wish you would've called me. I hate I found out about the baby at my dumpster along with everyone else. By the time I arrived, the news reporters were driving away. I would've liked to put my spin on things, so my business doesn't take a negative hit."

"Sorry. Everything happened so fast."

"Well, it appears things turned out okay."

At my register, I experience the shortcomings of living in a small town. A sea of rumors rage into flames of gossip. Customer after customer recognizes me. I nearly swallow my tongue when Eli shows up. "Hey, beautiful. I saw you on the news last night."

"Oh, yeah?" My suspicions ramp up. I look for any sign indicating he knows something. "I can't believe someone could act so uncaring."

He nods, shifting his weight from one foot to the other. "That's unbelievable."

I lean in closer. "Do you know something?"

"Who, me? No. But I would like to know if you'd go with me to a concert tomorrow?"

Surprised, I sputter, "Y-you w-want to go out with me?"

"Do you have a boyfriend or another reason we can't hang out?"

I release a calming sigh. This may be an opportunity for me to find out if he was the one who left Grace near the dumpster. I search his expression. "Okay."

"There's a summer concert at Scissortail Park. I think we should check it out. Are you game?"

"Yep. I love good music."

"I have practice until late. My brother and his girlfriend will ride with us. Can you meet me at the gym?"

"Yeah, I guess."

"I'll see you tomorrow, beautiful."

After several customers, Eartha unloads items onto my conveyor belt. "Hey, sweetie-sweet."

"Eartha, are you here harassing Mr. Barker again?"

"Child, that man loves me. He just doesn't know it yet." She tugs the large black diamond 'E' on a chain around her neck.

I laugh at her audacity.

"Last night, I promised to put my P.I. hat back on and help you find out who left the baby. I may have a lead. Why don't you come by tomorrow, I should be able to tell you what I've dug up?"

"Tell me now, who's the suspect?"

"Be patient. I'm close to pinpointing the who's, how's, and why's."

"Tomorrow. Okay. It may be late. I have a date with this guy I just met." I flutter my eyelashes.

"What about Terrence?" she purses her lips. "Sweetie-sweet, he's in love with you. I know he's your childhood friend, but don't tell me you can't see that."

"Are you investigating me and Terrence too?"

"It's in my nature to investigate everyone." She does her high-pitched, wicked witch laugh until she reaches the sliding doors. Parked in the handicap space closest to the store, I observe her pop the trunk of her Prius, load in her purchases, and drive off with the hatchback still up.

I apologize to the customer in line while I run from behind my register. Someone else flags her down and assists her in lowering the hatch.

A grateful sigh blows over my lips. Eartha. What am I going to do with you?

~ * ~

On my drive home, I call Terrence. "Eli dropped by the store and invited me to go with him to a concert at Scissortail."

"Didn't you tell me you think he's Grace's father?"

"Yeah. But I don't know for sure. Maybe by going out with him, I will learn more."

"You sound a little too happy for this to be a crime-solving outing."

I tease, "Terrence, are you jelly?"

"Maybe. Yeah, a little."

"Don't be jealous. I'm doing this for Grace."

"Um, huh." Doubt rings loud in Terrence's tone.

~5~

Sweaty moist air hits me in the face as soon as I open the gym's door. Yells and blowing whistles assault my ears as I make my way to the bleachers. At last, Eli runs off the floor, holding up a finger. "Fifteen. A quick shower and I will be out before you miss me."

Water droplets glisten in his short wavy hair when he emerges, wearing a green camouflage t-shirt and jeans. A younger, and a tad shorter, version of himself follows behind. A female runs across the floor and joins the group. I stand, smoothing down my purple shirt and denim shorts, as Eli stops before me. "Bianca, this is my brother Ellis and his girlfriend Eva."

Really? More 'E' names? How will I ever figure this out? Grace may belong to one of these "E's. But which one?

I shake Ellis's hand. He and Eli could be twins. Eva, petite, cute, and extra giggly, hangs on to my arm, calling me her new best friend.

We follow Eli to his sporty black car. When everyone loads in, we head for the interstate. Twenty-five minutes fly by, and soon we reach Oklahoma City. The last time I visited here, my father was alive. Lots of updates occurred while I stayed in Honeyville.

Eli's hand slips into mine. No doubt, his firm grasp speaks to the way he handles a basketball. Our group treks the park's manicured grass. Strategically placed newly planted trees mark the landscape. Children run through sprouting water fountains. Not far away, stands a lake. People float in some type of foot-propelled boats, disturbing the swimming ducks. Laughter flows from a playground lined with towers and slides. Soon a music pavilion materializes on the horizon.

As the sun prepares to set, a crowd gathers for the outdoor concert, awaiting some multi-platinum singers to perform. We stand amid the gathering. Eli's cell rings. He answers, whispers for a short while, then disconnects. Releasing my hand, he says, "Stay here with Ellis and Eva. I'll be right back."

I feel betrayed. "Where are you going?"

Without acknowledging my question, he says, "Ellis, I'll be right back." Eli hurries off, ducking around the playground and the water fountains as he jogs toward his car.

The music draws my attention with captivating tempos filled with melodies that speak of love and heartbreak.

When the singer announces the last song, I glance around for Eli. His height aids my seeing him walking across the playground.

In seconds, he stands at my side. "Where have you been?"

"Taking care of business. How was the concert?"

"Fine." Suspicion rumbles in my stomach.

The crowd disperses. We find ourselves back in Eli's vehicle.

Conversations flow freely between Eli, Ellis, and Eva. I listen, trying to figure out which of them is Grace's parent.

We arrive at HU's gym, Eli walks me to my car and takes my hand. "I'm sorry, I couldn't enjoy the concert with you. Maybe we can go out again."

Jitters flutter my stomach. And not the good kind. I slip out of his grasp. "We'll see. I'm kinda busy right now with ..." Fumbling with my key fob, I hit unlock and slide behind the steering wheel. "...with stuff." I wave and speed away. Terrence picks up on the first ring. I say, "Where are you?"

"I'm on my way to Ms. Eartha's."

"Why?"

"I thought I'd better check on her since you were out dating a basketball player."

"Shut up. I'll meet you there."

"What did you learn?"

"Nothing. I just didn't get a good impression of him. We'll discuss it at Eartha's. See you in a few."

When I round the corner, the first thing I notice is Eartha's garage door standing open. I pull up behind Terrence's red SUV and get out.

"Bi! Don't come in here."

~6~

I stand beside my car. Terrence's quivering voice takes my focus from the warmth filling the night air, which speaks to the last day of June, as well as the glorious low-hanging moon, competing with the dimly lit lamppost on the corner.

"I mean it, Bi," he says, "stay outside."

Disregarding his command, I follow his voice and sprint to the garage.

The driver's door on Eartha's Prius stands open. I glimpse a leg as Terrence leans down, peering at something. He shakes his head with a tight frown spread across his face.

I stop at the arch of the garage. "What's wrong?"

"A crime has occurred."

"What do you mean?" I inch forward, fearing what I may see.

"Just stay back."

A force pushes me forward until I stand at his side. "Eartha!" My hand flies to my mouth as my heart thumps hard in my chest.

In the reclined front seat, she stares heavenward. The spark of life no longer shines in her eyes. Her mouth stands gaped, and her walking cane rests on her chest.

Feeling close to hysteria, I glance here and there, looking for the chain bearing the letter 'E' she always wears. But I do not see it.

"Terrence —"

"She's gone, Bi. We should call for help." He looks at me. "Call your uncle."

Lightheaded, my stomach rolls, and water replaces the joints in my knees. I stagger outside, barely making it outside of the garage before my belly empties into Eartha's flower garden.

Tremors rack my body. Several times, the cell nearly slips from my fingers as I dial Uncle Davis.

"Goddaughter, what makes you call this time of night? And please don't say you found another baby."

I gulp, trying to find my voice.

"Bianca. What's wrong? Where are you?"

"M-my fr-friend, Eartha is dead." Her address pours out like rain. "Help me, Uncle Davis."

"Stay on the phone. Tell me what you know."

"Nothing. Terrence and I just got here. Her garage door is up, and she's in her car. Looks like someone strangled her with her cane."

"Okay. Okay. You and Terrence need to stay outside and don't touch anything."

"I'm not sure, but we might have already touched stuff."

"I'll fix it. I'll fix it."

"How?"

"Let me worry about that. I need to make a few phone calls. Stay put. I'll be there in a few."

The call disconnects. Terrence appears at my side. His arms ease around me, drawing me into his chest.

I breathe in his cologne and release a sob. Another moan pushes up from my gut, then another. Before I can stop myself, I weep, blubbering out the heartache of finding a dear friend departed. Gone forever.

Sirens sound in the distance. Uncle Davis arrives in his black Ford Crown Vic, stopping in front of the driveway.

He gets out, sporting a deeply wrinkled white shirt. Holes show in the knees of his dark denim jeans. Not wearing his usual suit and tie, he looks different. Casting thoughts of his clothes aside, I run to him. But I stop short when two vans bearing the local news station logos come into view.

A look of annoyance twists my godfather's features. "I guess they heard about this over their radio scanner." Like a traffic cop, he directs them farther from the scene.

Patrol cars line the street. Officers jump out, guns drawn, and rush into the house. Returning without suspects, they string yellow tape across the front yard. A fire engine and an ambulance block the intersection. The chaos causes the neighbors to come out of their homes.

The same reporter who asked if I was Grace's mother sticks a microphone in my face. "Aren't you the person who found the baby? How coincidental? Now you've discovered a dead body. Can you tell us—"

"No interviews, please," Uncle Davis interrupts.

The man frowns. "But you said I could have the exclusive if—"

"I know what I said. Just hold off for now."

My breath hitches. My godfather just lied to my face! I turn to Terrence. His raised brows say he heard the contradiction too.

"Okay. Okay." Uncle Davis lifts his hands in surrender. "I need publicity, but not at the expense of your good name. Do you want me to make them leave?"

I shake my head. "They're here now." Grasping Terrence's arm, I ask, "Can we go?"

"You'll need to give a statement first." He beckons a police officer over. "Put them in your patrol car and find out what they know.

~7~

Wrapped in a towel, I wipe the steam from the bathroom mirror and stare at my reflection. Today is Eartha's funeral. If I didn't love her so, I would talk myself out of going.

In my bedroom, I blow out the vanilla-lavender candle that usually relaxes my mind and prepares me to face the world. Today it does not work. After removing my black sleeveless dress from my closet, I lay it on the unmade bed and sit beside it. Squeezing the corner of the purple comforter in my fist, I glance at the matching curtains and modern art I loved so much. Now it all seems like wasted efforts.

All week, I walked in a daze, concluding my life needs more. When my daddy told me over and again to build my hopes on eternal things, I never understood what he meant — until I looked into Eartha's lifeless eyes. Where did she go? What did she leave behind to help others? What does she regret not doing? How can I make my mark before the spark of life leaves me? And then where will I go?

My cell chimes and Terrence's name flashes on the screen.

"This is your fifteen-minute warning call."

Goodness, he knows me too well. "I'll be ready." I end the call and slip into the dress, dig earrings out of my jewelry box, wriggle my feet into my new purple tennis shoes, and walk back into the bathroom. After twisting my braids into an updo and applying lip gloss, I go to the living room to look for my mother.

She rises from the couch wearing a classy two-piece pantsuit. Sympathy shines in her eyes. "How are you feeling?"

"Numb."

I walk into her embrace. "Why would someone kill Eartha?"

"Like I've said every day this week, only God knows."

"And why wasn't she wearing her necklace? She loved it. It was the last gift from her beloved brother before he died." I swallow a sob. "Dear, dear, Eartha. She loved everybody."

"What do I always say?" Momma's hands rest on my shoulders as she holds me at arms-length and stares into my eyes. Together, we quote a portion of Job 1:21. "... the Lord gave, and the Lord hath taken away; blessed be the name of the Lord."

The scripture feels cold. I do not want Eartha taken away. I back away from Momma and turn to the window. Now I will never know the information she dug up. Who left baby Grace at the dumpster? Is that why they murdered her? Or was it a random act because of her, once again, forgetting to close her garage door?

Seeking answers leaves me exhausted. At the sight of Terrence's vehicle turning into the drive, I breathe a sigh of relief.

I climb into the backseat, letting Momma sit in front. Terrence reaches back and squeezes my hand. "We'll get through this together."

He has said those same words this whole week. Coming over and sitting with me on the front porch, lending his support. I cannot say how grateful I feel to have Terrence as a friend.

Soon we arrive at the church. The parking lot stands filled to near capacity. Terrence finds one of the few spots left. We enter the large white building and pause, staring at the wood grain casket.

Almost every pew stands filled. Terrence takes my hand and leads me to one near the back. I spot a bench closer to the front. Before I can say anything, Mr. Barker walks past, followed by Eli and Emmalyn. He points. "Grandson, we can sit here."

My mouth drops. Mr. Barker, is Eli's grandfather? I recall Eli saying his grandpa was the reason he enrolled in HU, I never asked for a name.

Did Eartha know?

Emmalyn scoots in beside Eli. Suspicion brews in my belly. Mr. Barker left early the night someone planted Grace at the dumpster. Did he do it for his grandson? No. Not dear Mr. Barker. But I cannot feel one hundred percent about anyone. Especially when I consider meeting Eli that same night. And Emmalyn shopped at the store around that same time, too.

I drop my head into my hands. Too much information to process.

"Are you okay?" Terrence pats my leg.

"Just trying to take it all in."

He intertwines our fingers. "I'm here."

"I know."

Uncle Davis shows up. We move down. He sits next to my mother and immediately takes her hand. My brows rise. When did they become so ... so friendly? Maybe suspicion runs in my veins. Everyone's a suspect.

Leo slides onto the bench next to Uncle Davis, forcing me to the opposite end.

The funeral begins, and I forget all my worries. Tears stream from my eyes at the kind words spoken about Eartha.

Before long, we stand at Terrence's vehicle. My mother crosses the two-lane street and goes to Uncle Davis, standing beside his dull black Crown Victoria.

Again, he takes her hands and draws her close. She turns to me. "Davis said he will take me home."

Befuddled, I gulp out, "Okay."

My godfather offers a big smile while digging into his pocket.

"Bi," Terrence's voice rises, "someone wants to buy my latest app."

"Really?" Unconcern sounds in my tone as my eyes stay on my mother and Uncle Davis.

That is when it happens. Time stands still.

From my godfather's pants pocket, Eartha's cursive 'E' glittering with the black diamonds falls to the ground.

Pointing. I cannot find my words. "Hers. Hers." I glance at Terrence, but he focuses on his phone. "Uncle Davis is the one who got it."

"No. We're still negotiating prices."

Oh. My. Goodness. "Terrence!"

"Bi, hold on a moment."

"Forget it."

Terrence nods and gets into his car.

Uncle Davis stoops to pick up the chain. I hurry in his direction. Stopping beside my mother, I ask, "What are you doing with Eartha's necklace?"

He tosses it from hand to hand. "I must've taken it, by accident, from the crime scene and forgot to turn it in."

I look at him from head to toe. That night he wore holey jeans, today he wears slacks. I can hardly catch my breath while listening to him tell the lie. The guilt on his face, which he works hard to hide, stands as further proof.

"So." I cross my arms. "You've kept the necklace for over a week, just carrying it around in your pocket?"

I glance at Momma, knowing she will back me on this. But she holds up a finger. "Give him a chance to explain, Bianca."

Throwing up my hands, I say, "Explain what? Something stinks … like a lie."

"Goddaughter." Uncle Davis growls.

I fling a look his way and double take.

He holds open his jacket, exposing his holstered weapon. His face transforms from caring into evil as he nods toward the car. "Get in."

"Who?" I glance at my mother and back at him.

He nods. "Both of you."

My mother steps closer to him. "There's no need for Bianca —"

"Both of you." He opens his back door. "Now!"

The word rings in my ear. I look around, glad to see Leo heading our way.

In a low, grave tone, Uncle Davis mumbles, "Don't say something you'll regret. Many people will get hurt." His eyes flit from Momma to me.

Leo stops beside us. "What's going on?"

Before I can answer, Uncle Davis grabs my mother's arm. She willingly goes to his side, as he says, "I thought I'd take my favorite people to the lake. We'll relax on my boat. Maybe enjoy a small picnic. Just hang out, getting reacquainted." An award-winning smile spreads across his face.

Wow. He sounds so believable. I do not want to endanger my mother or anyone else, so I keep my mouth shut and pray Leo reads the fear on my face.

Leo only glances down at the gold watch on his wrist. "I got to get back to the office. So, I'll see y'all later." He takes a step in my direction. "We still need to work on that chokehold. Tomorrow. Don't be late."

I glance at Uncle Davis. Will I be alive tomorrow? I nod from the backseat as my godfather closes the car's door.

Flashing his weapon again, Uncle Davis takes Momma by the elbow, and they walk around to the front passenger side.

Leo strolls to Terrence's SUV. My friend barely looks up from his phone as they talk and laugh.

I use my sixth sense and send mental messages. Help I'm being kidnapped. My extrasensory perception does not work. Neither my best friend nor my martial arts instructor picks up the vibe.

Uncle Davis closes Momma's door. "She turns to me. Let's not jump to conclusions."

"What's to conclude? He showed us his weapon and insisted we get in the car. We're being taken against our—"

Uncle Davis slides in behind the steering wheel. "Ready ladies?"

"I'm not. Terrence and I have plans."

"Not anymore." Uncle Davis starts the engine.

Leo always preaches never go to a second location with an attacker. Well, I think this qualifies as that, and I am letting it happen, mostly because my mother sits in the car with me.

Uncle Davis eases onto the street as if taking a Sunday morning drive. I glance back. Terrence still sits in his SUV, staring at his cell phone. I doubt he even knows we drove away.

Uncle Davis speaks to Momma. "Your daughter is too much like her father. That's just why he's not alive today."

My mother gasps.

Shifting forward in the backseat, I yell, "You killed my daddy?"

His head judders as if the loudness of my words hurts his ear. He holds out his hand. "Give me your phone, Bianca."

"No. Not until you tell me what happened."

"Same thing that's about to happen to you. Now, give me your phone."

My mother wipes a tear and repeats what Uncle Davis said. "The phone, Bianca."

I snatch it from a side pocket in my dress and hand it over. Immediately, he throws it out the window.

Through the rear windshield, I watch it bounce across the street. Leaning toward my mother, I ask, "Are you in this with him?"

She shakes her head. "I don't know what you're talking about."

"Yes, you do. How long have you known he was Daddy's murderer? Did y'all plan it together?"

Uncle Davis blows a long sigh. "She had nothing to do with it." He glances at Momma. "She's just as surprised as you. Ella, I need your phone, too."

Momma nods and places it in his hand. He chunks it out the window too. My mother forces a wobbly smile. But it seems to satisfy Uncle Davis.

"Ben's death catapulted my career. Who knew compensation for killing a partner would lead to promotion after promotion?" He chuckles. "That was an unexpected reward. And thanks to Emmalyn's secret baby, I will become mayor. What a coincidence that she dropped it off at the door of the police station just as I was exiting." He glances at me in the rear-view mirror. "I planted the backpack where I knew you would find it. As I expected, you called me for help." His low chuckle fills the confined space. "Emmalyn and Eli won't talk. Their careers are about to zoom to the skies. They won't jeopardize themselves for a baby." He shakes his head. "Eartha. That snooping old bitty questioned Emmalyn. She was going to expose me. I have come too far for her to spoil things. Yep, I had to put her out of commission."

Hyperventilation squeezes my lungs. Who is this cruel, insane person I call uncle?

We turn off the main street. Slowly, my godfather drives toward the old county bridge. The river below flows higher than normal because of recent heavy rains. A shiver races up my spine. I recall rumors of people walking into the area's thick foliage and never coming out. Families picnicking at the lake, never returning home. Dogs digging up bones from corpses of cold cases.

If I do not think fast, my mother and I will join the count of the missing and never found. Persuasively, as my godfather lies, he will make up something about us, and everyone will believe it.

The loud, rough ride over the old rusting bridge causes me to bounce around in the backseat. Momma holds onto the dashboard, and Uncle Davis slows his speed, dodging holes in the deteriorating concrete.

Impatiently, I look around, longing to make a move before time runs out, but I cannot think of anything other than what Leo told me. Work on your chokehold

Just as we hit the final bump, putting us on the other side, I shoot my arm around the headrest, sliding it under Uncle Davis's chin. I grab hold of my wrist with the other hand. With the car's seat between us, I cannot squeeze as tightly as I would like. Still, he gurgles as I work to shut off his oxygen.

The car zigzags and heads for the overgrown bushes and enormous trees. As Momma reaches for the steering wheel, she yells to me, "Hold on to him, Bianca."

I nod and squeeze tighter.

Uncle Davis mumbles something, claws at my arm, and stomps hard on the gas pedal.

The car jerks and shoots forward like a bullet. Everything passes in a blur. Momma fights to guide the vehicle down a narrow path. Thickets of limbs beat the door like drum majors.

Wild vines rip off the driver's side-view mirror. We barely miss several trees as we speed out of control. A hard bounce almost makes me let go, but I reinforce my grip, holding on for our lives.

"Ouch!"

Uncle Davis digs his fingers into my arm so hard it feels like he tears off a bear-sized chunk. I refuse to let go. As I wrestle to keep his air intake bare to none, I see his hand going for his weapon.

"Momma. Get the gun."

Her eyes flitter up and down as she steers the car while wrestling his hand away from the pistol.

A wide trunk tree causes a chill to race up my spine. "Momma! Look out!"

She yanks the steering wheel to the right. For a second, I float in the air. My arm wrapped around the headrest saves me from being flung to the opposite side of the car.

We barely missed the tree.

Uncle Davis growls like a wild animal. His large hand swipes the air several times, grappling, and pawing until he grabs a handful of Momma's hair. He drags her to his side. While she fights him, the car goes wild, shifting with every rise and dip in the terrain.

His wheezing lets me know it won't be long before he passes out, but my bruised arm grows tired.

Uncle Davis's long fingers cover Momma's face. Her teeth clamp down on his thumb. His soundless scream sends saliva gushing down my arm.

Yuck!

He jerks his hand from her mouth and makes a fist. In a flash, he draws back and lands a solid punch on her chin.

Her head hits the passenger side window as her eyes roll back.

"Momma!" my scream rebounds in the car.

She slides down the seat like melting snow from a rooftop, ending on the floor mat. With her head anchored between the seat and the glove compartment, she does not move.

The car continues out of control, and I do not know if I should keep holding on or check on my mother. The last words she spoke repeated in my mind. Hold on to him, Bianca.

I growl and tighten my grip. Uncle Davis jerks up his gun, reaching backward, he points the weapon over his head. I duck down as four bullets whiz past me, shattering the back windshield.

Peeking over the seat, I see the car heading for a huge mound of dirt. No way will we make it over the hill. At the last second, I release my grip and drop to the floor.

As the sharp sound of crunching metal reaches my ears, the impact of the crash molds me against the front seat with such force my teeth clatter, and everything goes black.

Awakened by a loud beeping, I drag myself up. Momma remains slumped in the same position. Uncle Davis lies bent forward; his head presses the horn.

"Momma."

She groans.

"Hold on. I'll help you." It takes several pushes to get the back door open. Leaning on the car's trunk, I trudge through the knee-high jungle. With every step, bushes bury my purple tennis shoes.

The backside and front sides of the car look like two different vehicles. The dirt hill bent the hood into a tent. Smoke comes from the engine. I grab the passenger side door. With all my strength, I pry it open. Ignoring the blaring horn, I help my mother out of the car.

She looks back at Uncle Davis. "Is he alive?"

He lies still as the dead with blood streaming from a gash in the middle of his forehead.

Not that I wish death on anyone, but I would not cry if Satan dragged this man to hell. He does not appear to be breathing, so I say, "I don't think so."

"Murderer." She spits blood from a split lip.

I turn in the direction that we came, following the mowed-down path the car made.

We make it to the last large tree we barely missed, and Momma puts up a hand. "I need to rest. My head is pounding. I feel nauseous." She sits on a raised root and drops her head between her knees.

At that moment, the woods grow silent. A tingle rushes up my spine. "Oh no, Momma. The horn stopped. He's alive."

"Maybe he fell over, or the battery died."

The driver-side door unexpectantly opens, washing away all doubt.

"Come on Momma, we cannot let him see us."

We duck to the opposite side of the tree and stay close to the tall bushes. I pray they cover us as we follow the car tracks.

In a clearing, we catch our breath. "Momma, there's the bridge. When we get across, we can flag down help."

"Too bad you won't make it that far."

Momma and I jerk around. Uncle Davis stands feet away, pointing his weapon.

Goodness, why didn't I grab his gun while I had the chance?

"Davis." Momma shows her palms. "You and I can go away from this lifeless town. Leave Bianca. No one will believe her, anyway."

"I will be mayor of this town." Limping, he passes Momma and stops before me. He brings up the gun, pointing it at my chest. "She'll keep talking until someone listens. She's too much like Ben."

"Please, Davis." Momma drops to her knees in the dirt.

He glances her way. I take advantage of the slight distraction and grab the gun with both hands. Using the disarming technique Leo taught, I twist the barrel toward him.

But Davis knows the counter move. Hooking his free arm around my wrist, he stops my ability to take away his weapon. He moves like a cat, pivots to my side, and lifts the pistol to my head.

Leaning forward, I barely make it out of the path of the bullet before the loud boom. My ears ring. I swing back my hand, pushing the gun away from me. We both spin. Again, with both hands, I grab the pistol and twist with all my might.

He reacts a nanosecond too slow to countermove. Now I will either break his finger stuck in the trigger guard, or he will release his grip. He holds on. I step closer, increasing the agony.

He groans. "Goddaughter, you're hurting me."

"I know."

He claws a path up my arm. But I cannot afford to succumb to pain. A moment ago, he tried to blow my head off.

I push against him more, but before I break his trapped finger, he releases. Moving away, he shakes his injured hand.

My heart nearly beats out of my chest with joy when I end up with the pistol. "Get on the ground."

"What are you planning?"

"Down!"

The graveling sounds of the unstable bridge say someone heads our way. I fear taking my eyes off Uncle Davis.

Momma jumps to her feet and runs toward whoever approaches.

On his knees, he says, "This won't work. I hope you know that."

"So maybe I should serve up justice now?"

"You don't have the guts."

"That could be true, I'm not uncaring as you."

Momma returns and pats my shoulder. I look up to find Leo and Terrence. Leo says, "What do we have here?"

"Arrest her." Uncle Davis points at me. "I turned my back. She took my gun."

At that moment, I realize how easy it would be to pull the trigger just to stop his lies.

"Bianca. I taught you well. Wouldn't you agree, Sims?" Leo pulls out his handcuffs and steps behind Uncle Davis. "Man. The department has had you under surveillance for a week. I never believed that lie about Ben's death. But after Eartha Johnson's murder, I asked our supervisor if we could bug your car, home, and office. We heard everything."

Leo takes the gun from me, putting it in his waistband. Then he yanks my godfather to his feet.

Terrence pulls me into his arms. "I tried tracking your phone. I knew if I got too close, he would be suspicious. When he threw away the cell phones, I wasn't sure where to look. But Leo knew."

Momma wraps her arms around Terrence and me. "God made you two for each other. Bianca, let's go file some long overdue charges."

~8~

"Who, in their right mind, gave you a baby?"

"You don't have to say it like that, Terrence." I glance at Grace lying in her crib. "But if you must know. My husband gave me the child."

"Who's your husband, I need to talk to that man."

A belly laugh, like Daddy's, flows from me. "You. Dear. You're my husband."

"In that case, it's okay. Is your mother coming today?"

I nod.

Easing the door closed, we leave one-year-old Grace sleeping in her nursery. Our walk takes us through our newly built home, out the French doors, to the large deck filled with outdoor furniture. We sit in a wicker love seat overlooking the well-tended yard.

After the incident, Terrence and I knew what we wanted. Eartha's death proved we did not have time to waste. And Momma spoke the truth when she said God made us for each other.

While planning our wedding, we enrolled in foster care classes. Shortly after saying, "I do", Grace came to live with us. Eli and Emmalyn agreed to an open adoption.

Terrence takes my hand. "You know how long I've waited to call you wife, Bianca Blake-King."

"Since grade school?"

"Since grade school."

His lips meet mine and I melt into his arms.

The noonday heat of summer wraps us in an unexpected breeze and I pray it never lets us go.

The Gifts of

Autumn

Attainment

Wisdom

Confidence

Middle Age

by Joe Scavetti

"Grandpa, what's Middle Age?" he asked as he went
dashing by.
"...being older than a kid and younger than being
old" was my reply.

"Oh" I heard as he raced from the room like a wild
thing fleeing a cage.
In the stillness, I pondered what it meant to me, my
own Middle Age.

I didn't see it coming until it was well past. I held
onto things more near;
Lost in the excitement of early grandkids and the
stress of a late career.

Middle Age was when, one by one, my "gonnabe's"
became "neverwas"
And I learned that Mom was right, "Some things are
as they are, just because."

That's when my "salt and pepper" hair became a
"distinguished gray"
And my steadfast, rigid beliefs began to lean, to
waver, and then to sway.

My appearance in the mirror was no longer mine – it
 was that of my Dad.
Others seeing the likeness told me so and their
 observations made me glad.

Middle Age - years that bridge our youthful rise into
 our physical decline;
When the tenants I couldn't tolerate I came to see
 were actually "just fine."

It's when I learned that the World had more
 problems than I alone could fix.
But these details aren't important when the inquirer
 is only six.

Stealth of Fall

by Darlinda Hagens

Wedged between sunburns and snowdrifts.
Fall rides the autumnal equinox.
Much like a middle child's cries, unnoticed,
There's a gradual change in the aging paradox.

Creeping in unaware, Fall steals sunshine from days,
Leaving wilted footprints of yellow, red, and brown.
With the stealth of a ninja, it strikes without
    warning.
Leaf after leaf dies, dropping silently to the ground.

Yet, stealthy Fall serves as a bridge.
A hiatus between summer and winter.
Seasons rely upon it to pass over.
Homage to Fall, our change defender

.

50 Candles

by B.S. Adamsons

The chemist shop's calendar on the wall showed no markings for the square dedicated to this Saturday. It was to be the same as every other weekend day in his sleepy town, till the knock at the side door interrupted that quiet. A gangly youth stood outside it, awkwardly holding a square white box.

"Can I help you?"

"Happy birthday, Mister Murphy. Here." he mumbled, handing over the box. "There's a card too," he added quickly as he searched a jacket pocket.

Holding the box in one hand and the card in the other, Joe turned and found he had to push folders and loose papers across the kitchen table to make room to set them down. The delivery was a first for him. He slowly opened the box and stared at the number written in frosting, surrounded by five candles. It shouted "50" from the cake, nestled in the Waack Bakery's open box.

Joe fumbled around the jumbled drawer for a knife to cut open the envelope. An old man, with a beard down to the ground and bending over a walking cane decorated the front of the card. Puzzled, he opened it. A smile widened as he read each printed humorous insult. At the bottom in bright green pen - "Happy Birthday Joe. Wish we could be with you on this special day. With love from your baby sisters, Marie and Maureen."

The handwriting had Maureen's unmistakable bold strokes. Joe wiped specks of moisture from his reading glasses. A lot of effort had been spent for the card to arrive in time at the bakery on Main Street for this delivery. The Murphy family branches continued to spread across the country. Maureen was in Brisbane, helping with her newest grandchild. Marie was on a grandmother duty call in Perth.

As Joe looked at the card and cake, he could not help but think about his past. He reminisced about his youthful happy days and some that later left him scarred.

Joe was the oldest in the family, but from the start, he was the one needing help in practical matters. Pre-occupation with plans to eliminate the world's problems got in the way of remembering keys or coats when leaving the house. His life's mission started in kindergarten as he rushed into the circle of bullies to rescue Australia's newest arrival. With a driver's license, lost in some pocket, he drove to meetings all over the state encouraging voting or braved winter's assaults, jacketless, on a Union's protest line.

Vietnam took over Joe's life when refugees started to arrive in Australia. He inherited the family home when a stroke took his father from it. Just a year later, Joe's mother became his child. He constantly was on the alert as to her whereabouts. Finding daily care help for her was difficult, even though he worked at the government's Department for Health and Human Services. The town's smallness allowed others to notice Kathleen wandering alone and singing joyfully as she picked dandelions along a road. Joe's phone number was known by all and helped return his mother home. Heaven called her as Joe turned forty.

Refugees filled any vacuum left by the early departure of his parents. Empty rooms could not be, if there were new arrivals from Asia. Joe's family grew with the love from children calling him Ba Joe or Papa Joe. Bent elders spoke their love through hand motions and misted eyes. Breaks from the office depleted any savings as he volunteered in Vietnam and increased his chosen family.

On one such trip, the new landscapes captivated Joe. He understood heaven when in Dà Lat, high among hills, lakes and waterfalls. Then peace entered his soul with the beauty of Vietnam's coastline in Nha Trang, made lush by tropical rain showers. His created family expanded yearly guaranteeing he never would be hungry or lonely. Ties strengthened each time someone discovered that he had helped their cousin or friend. Joy and pain filled his body and soul over the years as he volunteered.

One person brought pain to Joe's heart instantly. They had met on a humid evening in Nha Trang, as he waited for another volunteer at a bar.

Feet away a sparrow of a young girl, in high stiletto heels, moved from foot to foot with frightened eyes darting back and forth from a close-by table covered with beer bottles. From it, a lily-white trio of guys tossed words and whistles at her. Joe knew what could happen and caught the waif's eye. He patted the stool next to him. Her shoulders lowered and a brief smile flicked across the red lips.

As the petite form came closer, Joe searched his pockets. He knew he must make her feel safe.

"Looks like you need help. I'm Joe Murphy and work for this group," he said softly, holding up the found lanyard. The puzzled look made Joe add, "Do you speak English?" His gentle tone was meant to assure the woman of her safety now.

"I speak English. My name Tuyen. I happy you here. Foreign men like that make me fright." She bowed her head, with lowered eyes, in gratitude.

Joe's empathy, in full force, made him suggest a glass of Coca Cola, and his unexpected companion accepted. In between sips her breathing calmed and she answered his questions. Her eyes lowered often but she, in whispered tones, related the years of moving from city to city in search of her family. Fear reappeared in her eyes when she spoke of the dangers encountered as a lone woman. Joe's soul heard the unspoken call for help.

By midnight Joe accepted that his drinking pal wouldn't arrive and concentrated on assessing Tuyen's situation. He didn't want this vulnerable creature on the street and in danger at that hour. She mentioned her rented room in a boarding house close by. Still feeling the need to protect his newest friend, Joe escorted her to it and wrote down his phone number on a napkin from the bar.

As the days passed, thoughts of Tuyen invaded Joe's mind and heart. Daily, he provided her meals and even protection from the elements with an umbrella. The fragile-looking woman's repayment to her benefactor was as a guide to the city's beauty, unseen by foreigners. Joe's need to rescue her grew with each passing day. He knew he could help her to a better life with his means and contacts.

Traditional roles for men and women, engrained from Joe's childhood remained at the forefront of his thinking. Tuyen's attention to his comfort and her acceptance of his protection seemed to make her happy. A desire for a life's companion awakened. The suggestion to go to Australia produced the broadest of smiles. The necessity of a marriage to make it happen, as required by the government, caused a frown, then a cautious smile, before a nod.

With understanding of the system, in four months, Joe stood at Tullamarine airport, awkwardly clutching in his sweating hand a posy of fragrant Daphne. In another month, Joe and Tuyen stood before Father Foley at St. Patrick's, to exchange vows. The wedding, though small, had a traditional gown, flowers and cake quickly arranged by Marie and Maureen, once the surprise of the announcement wore off.

The stooped priest's smile reached all the way to Ireland as he pronounced them husband and wife, adding that God had taken His sweet time to find Joe a suitable life partner.

"In a foreign country at that!" he said with a raised brow. "Now I can go to my eternal reward in peace," were the priest's parting words.

Joe saw a new start in the autumn of his life. His bride, twenty years younger, presented the possibility of adding to the Murphy clan. Joe knew that patience to start a marriage would be needed since it all happened so quickly. He reminded himself daily that Tuyen needed time to adjust. A spare bedroom became a corner of Vietnam, with a shrine for Tuyen's lost family, and her bed.

A neat house and prompt meals on the table Tuyen saw as her only daily duties. With eyes always downcast she refused her husband's invitations to join the Australian social world. Her social contacts were on the phone and in Vietnamese. Joe often heard laughter when he walked into the house after a long day at work, but the call always swiftly ended when he appeared. He willed himself to be content with a timid wife in tidy, comfortable surroundings and having a body well fed.

Months of waiting for a true wife finally made Joe desperate. One quiet evening he brought her the favorite Coke and slowly lowered himself on to the chair across the room.

"Tuyen are you sick? Do you need help? I can take you to the best doctors."

Tuyen straightened her body, with hands tightly clasped in her lap and eyes downcast whispered, "Yes, I not well."

"I can take some time off next week and we can go to Melbourne. Marie lives there. Do you want to talk to her and tell her what's wrong so that we can find the right doctor? I don't understand women's problems."

The silence stretched for what seemed to be an eternity before Tuyen looked up. "I not speak English good. In Sydney doctor good for Vietnamese ladies."

Joe thought a five-hundred-mile drive to Sydney would be worth the time, to have a true wife.

"We can get there for an afternoon appointment if we set out early in the morning. Why don't you set up an appointment and tell me when, so I can get time off?"

"Plane… job need you."

The suggestion made sense. But Joe did not want Tuyen alone in a big city. Maybe Maureen could make a three-hour drive from Canberra to help her new sister-in-law.

"I can get Maureen to meet you in Sydney and drive you to your appointment and help you with the doctor."

"No!" was the emphatic response. "She not understand Vietnamese, and children to take care."

"I wasn't thinking. I just worry about you and want to make life easier for you." Joe drew in a resigned breath. "Let me know the date you need the plane ticket for."

The appointment date was set in days and Joe saw a happier mood in his wife as they drove to the airport.

In broken English, Tuyen explained the need for an overnight stay and that the doctor's office had arranged it with a Vietnamese family close by.

As days and weeks passed, no report from the doctor's visits or a diagnosis appeared. Joe's awkwardness about such matters stopped him from asking. After four visits to Sydney, Joe was no wiser as to what problem kept his young wife from his bed.

A decade ago, Joe had sponsored Mai, another Vietnamese refugee, and her family to relocate in Australia. He thought if she visited with Tuyen, woman to woman, the problem might be solved quicker.

Joe's nervousness ended when Saturday arrived. He casually told his wife he was meeting a friend in town and would be back in an hour or so. No mention was made that the friend was Mai who had driven all the way from Melbourne. He needed to see Mai's happy face and get her wise advice. She had successfully made the adjustment in a strange land, during her ten years here.

Time, over coffee, flew as Joe explained his dilemma. Then Mai followed Joe to his house. She assured him that it would only take her a few minutes to find the problem. They both parked on the street. Through the open side door, laughter and Tuyen's voice exited clearly. Mai quickly pulled Joe back and an index finger flew to her lips.

Mai pushed Joe behind her and listened in silence, as the loud phone conversation continued, interspersed with joyful laughter. She stayed motionless for what seemed to Joe to be an eternity. Silence returned to the kitchen until a chair scraping on the wood floor broke it. Joe jumped as Mai bolted into the house and grabbed Tuyen by the shoulders.

She shook her mercilessly and pelted the younger woman with angry words Joe did not understand.

Despite numerous trips, Joe never learned Vietnamese, and now stood with his mouth open in the doorway. He only knew Mai as a calm and wise person. She was now a fiery dragon. Tuyen sunk lower on the kitchen chair and whispered responses to apparent questions from Mai. Joe used the door frame to hold himself up as his knees weakened. When the final storm of words ended, Tuyen rose quickly from the kitchen chair, and furtively left the room. Joe stood unmoving with a furrowed brow looking at Mai. She brushed her linen skirt, as if tidying up after a difficult task.

"Come bạn bẻ," she said, extending her hand and led Joe to the living room. In a daze Joe followed and sunk into the stuffed chair and waited. Fear about the explanation of the past five minutes showed on his face. Mai lowered to the floor next to him.

"I am very unhappy you were deceived Joe. When we arrived and I heard Tuyen's words, a signal went off. That's why I made you stop. Quickly I understood that the girl was talking to a lover. She was joyous that she is in Australia and could visit him by pretending to go to a doctor in Sydney. When I asked questions, I found more. The lover came over a year ago, but since he didn't have any papers, he could not sponsor Tuyen. Then you came along Joe, and a plan was made."

Joe could not breathe, and words could not form. Mai leaned forward and patted his lifeless hands.

"Tuyen says she is sorry she did such a bad thing and wants me to ask you for forgiveness. She said you are a very, very good man and deserve happiness."

Only a nod came from the man sunk in the chair.

"As the girl does not have a family or a strict mother to show her the correct path, I told her to pack her things. I will take her to my house."

Joe finally drew in a deep breath.

"My heart hurts. I can't even say goodbye to her." Two big hands covered his eyes. He stood up, shook the moisture from his fingers and squared his shoulders.

"It might be best if I go for a long walk. When I see your car gone, I'll come back."

The annulment took two years.

The loud kitchen phone woke Joe from his past.

"Happy birthday young man. Did the cake make it?" came clearly from Queensland.

"That was a shock. It is sitting on the table here."

"I have Maureen on another line, so why don't you light the candles, and we'll sing the required song before you blow them out."

Joe retrieved the box of matches by the gas stove and quickly lit the five candles.

The family's singing quality had not changed over the years, and Joe felt the old family bond as he blew out the candles. He forgot to make a wish.

"What have you done so far today to celebrate the big day?" asked Maureen.

"Just revisiting the past half century."

"That was a busy and interesting one for you, mate," chimed Marie.

"You did so much for others, Joe. Time to use the next half for yourself," was the advice from his older sister.

"Happy birthday Joe," they said in unison before the phone line went silent.

Joe picked up the knife and cut the cake.

"Chocolate cake for breakfast is appropriate today," he stated aloud and took a big bite. Wiping crumbs from his lips, he headed for his computer.

How quickly the years had disappeared. And what had he done with his life? Asia had always fascinated him with the different scenery and humble people. Now might be the time to explore it more. He started a search with "China."

Joe had accumulated weeks of holiday time, and even a nest egg since he stopped travelling to refugee camps. His growing computer skills found him an affordable packet, with an English-speaking guide and places that, to him, were only names.

"Can you get high on chocolate cake? What did I just do? Yes! I'll take Marie's advice and do something for myself before the autumn of my life changes to winter. The hair is beginning that already."

***

Arriving in Beijing, the vastness and density of people overwhelm Joe. The voices around him are just chatter, and panic starts in his stomach. He relaxes when he sees a short, dark-haired woman, in her forties, holding a large sign with letters he recognizes as his name. With a bow she introduces herself as Ah Lam, his guide for the next ten days. She controls his world as she retrieves his luggage and commands a taxi to take them to the skyscraper high hotel. Joe's jaw unclenches at the reception desk when he hears English from behind it.

Ah Lam bows slowly in farewell, and reminds Joe that the next day's tour will start promptly at 8:00 AM from the lobby.

Joe exits the elevator on the dot of 8:00 AM to see a group surrounding his guide from the previous day. Men with neat ties and women in well pressed dresses and jackets intermingle with casual dress and sneakers in the circle of people.

Ah Lam stands in the middle, counting.

"Good we have twelve now that Mr. Murphy has arrived. Please follow me."

New sights, and getting to know people from England and America, pack the day. Joe wipes the sweat from his face each time the group retreats to the air-conditioned minibus, between walks into China's past.

At the end of three days, he sends a prayer of gratitude, to whatever god is around, for the hotel's modern comforts and the chance to review the dozens of photos taken on the Great Wall, in the Forbidden City, the Temple of Heaven and at the Summer Palace.

In the morning's light, Joe examines the Terracotta Army and decides that age fifty is not that old, after all. The army men have been standing since 210 BCE in Xian. A day in Zhangjia brings relaxation in nature's untouched beauty in the mountains.

By the time the tour reaches Shanghai, the twelve have fallen into groups of twos or threes. Joe is left alone and often finds himself with Ah Lam, automatically extending a hand to help her up and down steps. Always the professional, she never allows her personal life or views to escape during their conversations.

Visits to museums and the Jing'an Temple pack the final day and their stories reflect political changes over twenty centuries. The temple squeezes in between skyscrapers of a twenty-six million people city. A peaceful respite in the Yuyuan Gardens refreshes Joe.

An extravagant dinner on The Bund marks the group's final meeting. Along the expansive edge of the Huangpu River, lights glimmer or blaze as addresses and phone numbers are exchanged. Joe finds himself seated next to Ah Lam at the large round table. The tour guide's neutral façade breaks when his enthusiasm for her country shows on his beaming face. Joe eagerly relates to her how the tour has started a thirst to learn more and maybe visit China further. She, in turn, talks about her life in different parts of China and offers her personal email to send for more information. She apologizes that her written English might be faulty.

The first email from Joe gives a litany of questions about China. The answer to his opening question of "How are you?" comes in a month. The cracked door of correspondence opens wider as two years pass and Ah Lam's English improves enough to give Joe a full portrait of her dreams and goals.

Joe learns that her name means "peace" and she longs for it in a changing country. Calm arrives in her life with the disappearance of a gambling ex-husband. She supports her son and aging parents. A bigger and freer world has opened up to her with each group of tourists met. She wants that for herself.

Skype expands the friendship, as the months turn into three years of interaction. Joe likes how Ah Lam fits into his home on a computer screen. Ah Lam becomes familiar with it through the same screen during frequent visits.

Friendship turns to love, then to marriage, and again Joe waits at Tullamarine airport. The bouquet of golden chrysanthemums crush in the first embrace. Ah Lam melts into Joe's house and takes charge. Order and efficiency banish the bachelor chaos, and Joe does not mind the change. She still needs to help her family in China, and Joe is amazed as to how his wife finds work at the meat processing site, works weekends at the local Chinese restaurant, and yet has time to keep him happy.

A year vanishes quickly, to Joe's shock. That night's dinner is elaborate, to remind him of their anniversary. Together they wash the dishes by hand and turn down the bed together.

Joe comfortably leans on the stack of pillows arranged carefully by his wife. She hands him his book and glasses, gently touches his cheek with her lips and slides under the covers to fall into instant sleep. Slowly Joe opens the book. A folded paper falls out. He doesn't remember using it as a book marker and unfolds it to satisfy his curiosity. The writing is familiar.

A long time ago in a lonely and prosperous world two people met. Great distance was between them. Time made it disappear and they married. Two people very happy, very loving because they know each other's feelings and happiness. Everyday kiss, hug every day no matter how many days. Two people sincerely in love.

You travel the world to know other country. Anyone who needs help you give. Poor and innocent children and bad family situation you fix. Husband, I admire your life and aspirations and good behavior. Your life is goodwill and assistance to the world.

I hear you thank God and what you say Beloved Wife do for your life. When I look in your eyes I see your love and your worry about my life issues so strong.

My dear husband, my next life I want to meet you again. Once again, I love you.

Joe clutches the note to his chest to calm his heart's powerful beating. Slowly he leans over and gently kisses the forehead of his sleeping wife. He places the book, protecting the love note, carefully on the nightstand and he turns off the light. Peace enters his life and stays, reminding him that love can come in every season.

Grace in Autumn

by Darlinda Hagens

Carrying a mug of pumpkin spice flavored coffee, I open the front door and step onto the porch of my mother's house. She left the place to me, but a month after her passing, I still can't bring myself to say, "My home."

A chilly breeze rustles the leaves that fell from the huge tree overhanging the yard. In two weeks, we celebrate Thanksgiving, but I do not know if I will ever celebrate again. Since my mother's sudden passing, I question the value of everything. So many unanswered questions.

My friends say, "That's how the grieving process works."

But knowing does not stop the ache in my heart or the need to feel Mom's arms wrapped around me.

I stare into the skies. The rising sun holds the promise of a beautiful day. Mom's matter-of-fact voice invades my thoughts. "Girly-pooh, what do you have to be sad about? When I was your age, I considered it the summer of life. A time to take all you've learned and apply it to building your nest egg. Because when you cross over into the fall of life, like me, if you're not prepared for winter, expect hard times."

Mom had a way of talking in circles. That's probably one thing I miss most.

I rush back inside and dress for work. When I get in my car, I find I have left the headlights on and drained the battery. Not the best start to my morning. Instead of worrying my friends, I decide to ride the city bus. It stops only three blocks away.

For the first time in a long time, I sit on the bench, waiting. An elderly woman, carrying several bags, wearing a man's brown double-breasted overcoat, sits beside me. She moves in much too close. And I wonder if I should have bitten the bullet and called a friend to jump my car. I forgot how many people with mental health issues use this mode of transportation. I can almost see my mother shaking her head at my reasonings. She hated it when I would lump a demographic of people into one classification.

The woman places all the items at her feet. One bag, holding an assortment of colorful flowers, falls over. She uprights it, then places a large black purse in her lap.

As she digs inside, I scoot down, giving her elbow room while preparing to do battle. I plan to wrestle her to the ground if she pulls out a weapon.

Instead, she drags out an old picture in a 4x6 frame. We both stare at the handsome man posing in a fedora hat and the exact brown overcoat the bag lady wears today.

She sighs several times, and I can tell her heart feels heavy too. So, I ask. "Is that a relative?"

She nods. "My husband. A good man." A tear rolls down her cheek. "Today is the first anniversary of his death."

"Oh, I'm sorry."

"Don't be sorry, dear, he lived a good life. God called, and he went home."

I want to question how she could know for sure. And where was home? On a cloud? In heaven? On earth? Under the earth? But I left her to her grief.

"I see you have more questions, dear. Ask. Ask away."

After only a second of hesitating, I blurt out, "My mother died last month, and I feel confused about all the death stuff. How do we know where people —"

"Souls, dear. Souls."

"Okay. Souls. Where do they go? How do we know?"

"That's a good question. If we trust the words in the Bible, Ecclesiastes 12:7 says, '…and the dust returneth to the earth as it was, and the spirit returneth unto God who gave it.'"

"How much trust can I put in the Bible? Does it say how I can get to where Mom is?"

"More complicated questions." She places the picture back in her bag. "Most of the hard questions take faith." She smiles and shakes her head. "When my Silas first passed away, I went around and around, questioning everything, asking God why. But you know what I figured out as I walk through the autumn of life?"

I shake my head.

"God doesn't owe us an explanation. We are his creation. We're born, we love, and we die. In between those times, if we're blessed with something extra, we should consider it cream. If the Almighty blesses you with family and friends who love you. Consider it cream."

"Cream?"

"Cream is the grace God adds on top."

The bus pulls to a stop and I walk to the door. The lady remains seated.

"Are you coming?" I ask.

"No. I need to sit here and think about my own words." She waves a hand. "I'll catch the next one."

Autumn Walk

by Carla Guthrie

Summer had its last hurrah a few weeks ago with a portentous storm that stripped the dust off of roofs and turned the cars parked in the alleyway as glossy as patent leather. The earth has not yet recovered from the dousing it received, nor has the sky, now a squeaky-clean blue. The sun has obliged the curtain call as well, and it rises a little later and sets a little earlier.

I walk on the boulevard as I've started doing recently, relishing the fact that the buildings no longer radiate stifling heat from their massive concrete walls, and I make my way to the park on this early Wednesday morning. It has been only a month since I have retired and the shift feels odd. I haven't gotten accustomed to the pace of unscheduled time. I still wake up at the crack of dawn out of habit and busy myself to get ready, while my husband tosses and turns as his body also signals to him that it is time to start a new day. His day is still one of hours of work, always more than eight as he owns a hardware store.

It has only been a month, but it feels as if I've been catapulted into a new dimension in which time has stretched. I feel that I am losing the tactile memory of the little hands of my kindergarteners. They weren't mine, really, but it felt as if they were. Each morning I'd greet them at the door and they'd respond with an enthusiastic, "Good morning, Mrs. O'Leary."

A dog who has broken loose from his owner jumps up at me, interrupting the nostalgic reverie. I have reached the park without realizing it and wonder what I've missed savoring on the way. Before retiring I had fantasized that I would be present each moment, that I would drink time slowly, paying attention to details that the hurried, harried life of commuting by subway had denied me for so many years. I had not taken into account the magnetic power of the past that keeps dragging me back to the comfortable familiar sensations of a well-established routine.

The owner of the dog, a young woman attired in leggings and a sports bra, reaches us as the pup plays a "catch-me-if-you-can" game running circles around me.

"I'm sorry. He gets so excited around people. It's not very often I take him running with me in the park."

I smile at her and attempt to pet the wiggly mass of fur.

"It looks like he made you work up quite a sweat," I say, noticing the perspiration glisten on her bare skin. She smiles at me in agreement.

"Yeah, but at least things have started to cool down." She grabs the leash, damp from trailing in the dewy grass.

She is right, the air this morning has a distinct nip, harbinger of what is to come. I reflect on the encounter. Perhaps, if I can't direct chubby little hands as they form letters, I should get a dog to take on walks. I quickly dismiss the idea; Henry would never go for that. A sudden breath of wind catches my dress and presses it against my legs. The coolness sifts through the fabric and makes me feel alive. I keep walking with the breeze accompanying me through this new experience of sunshine on a midweek morning. The benches are deserted at this early hour and I wonder if they will welcome tired people as the day goes on. I imagine old men with their canes resting, tired from exerting their slowing bodies. Or perhaps businessmen on their break from staring at numbers on computers, grounding their minds after being suspended on the fiftieth floor of some skyscraper dominating the city. I realize my thoughts are wandering again, this time into the future rather than the past. I'm finding out that the brain is not static, it vacillates between yesterday and tomorrow. It is more difficult than I expected to stay anchored in the present, to seize the day.

A riotous laugh jerks me back from my pondering and I pause searching to whom it belongs. I spy a couple in the middle of a grassy field. A plaid blanket spread underneath them and books open in front of them. Students. I catch myself grinning as they laugh about some joke I cannot catch from the distance. Their hilarity is contagious and I giggle to myself.

"Hey lady," the young man calls to me.

I stop and embarrassed by my intrusion in their private moment of joy, I wave feebly.

"Do you know anything about organic chemistry?" He asks loudly.

"No, just a retired kindergarten teacher here." I shoot back.

The girl sitting next to him claps her hand onto his mouth obviously embarrassed by his audacity. He wriggles out of her grasp and, with a flourish, yells in my direction.

"Hats off to you! That's where the magic of learning starts."

They wave wildly as I resume walking. I wave back, this time with more gusto, empowered by that unexpected boost of confidence. I've decided that next time anyone asks, I'll leave out the "just" and stick to the facts.

The heads of flowers that were once in bloom droop, brown and dry. They have exhausted their spring and summer task of prettying the place and are now intent at spreading seeds or growing dormant to live another spring next year. I wonder if now that I am retired, I can dedicate some time to growing things on the patch of dirt in front of our townhouse. The balance between doing nothing and filling the time with yet more activities teeters again towards the busyness side. Human nature perhaps abhors idleness.

My steps turn from the thud on the stony path to a satisfying squishy sound as I reach a patch of fallen leaves relinquished by a large ash tree stretching over the trail. It's beginning, the trees have started the annual ritual of shedding their vestments. I relish the noise my feet make as I step on the soft carpet of waterlogged foliage. Fall is fast approaching. On my last day at work, I saw the first leaf swirl slowly to the ground as I packed my books and mementos into cardboard boxes. As I closed the last lid on my career, I felt my heart follow the yellow leaves in their slow descent. I had hugged everybody and taken a last glance into the classroom, empty and ready for a fresh coat of paint. I wondered if the passion and love I had put into teaching would still echo from its walls. Life is change though; I need to release my grip on what I don't have any more in order to receive the season that awaits me.

A gust of wind twirls among pyramids of leaves that a park keeper has raked into piles on the grass. I watch them take flight and scurry on the pavement. My emotions scatter with them and my breath catches as I let go of the knots in my heart. I so want to be ready and excited for this new phase in life, but I waver, frightened by the looming unknown. I follow an airborne leaf and watch it land in the pond. I change direction and stand on the border of the rippling pool. Birds hop around on the sloping bank searching for nourishment while a duck, tail up out of the water, peruses the bottom. Perhaps, I too should skirt my new circumstances before plunging in. I am a timid bird, not a bold duck.

Suddenly, a splash startles me out of my musing. The shrill cry of a small child accompanies another rock hitting the water.

"No, no, Tommy. Don't throw rocks."

I watch the mother grab the boy's hand to prevent him from hurling yet another missile in my direction. She apologizes to me. I smile, but I refrain from condoning the act with the usual 'It's okay'. I don't want to hinder that precious teachable moment. I am pleased to see the young woman redirect her son's attention to the beauty of nature. They walk toward a berm where a variety of plants are clumped on its slopes. I listen to her read the little markers. The little boy claps his hands as he catches the excitement her voice effuses. It's liberating. One knot, the one that holds fast my concern that I can no longer transmit a love of learning to young minds, unravels and melts in a mottled puddle of sunshine coming through the branches of an elm still donning most of its leaves.

I resume my walk. With slow steps I turn toward the incline of the small bridge that spans over the bicycle path. I reach the top of its arched back and lean on the railing, a tangle of vines wraps around it providing a soft spot to rest my elbows as my hands hold my head filled with tumultuous thoughts. The vantage point affords me a broad view of the park. I find the landscape restful with its muted colors. The sparse human presence keeps me from getting distracted and I allow myself to finally drink in the scenery. My lungs expand and the cool moist air rushes in to tingle them awake. It is indeed a fine morning. I think of Henry, sitting behind the counter doling out screws and bolts and I wish he could be here instead, to enjoy the spectacular view with me. It's time to head back. There's grocery shopping to be done and a hot meal to prepare for Henry, who deserves some pampering after years of cold sandwiches and leftovers. But I don't want to go yet. I cross the bridge and head toward the tunnel of wisteria that leads to the other end of the park. As I walk under the unruly jumble of runners intertwining in and out of a thick web, I try to imagine how glorious it is in the summer when it blooms.

I feel the chill raise the hairs on my arms as I saunter in the shade. I really don't want to leave this place. My mother would accuse me of the dreaded sin of dawdling. I set a goal for the end of the tunnel, then I will circle back on the trail between the rocks. As I come around the bend, yellow tape bars the way. I pause to figure out a detour. An elderly man heading toward the wisteria tunnel, guessing my quandary offers, "If I were you, I would walk a few more yards and take the trail that cuts through the path lined with chrysanthemum." He winks and shuffles off. I don't particularly care for chrysanthemums, but his wink has stirred my curiosity. There are several shorter and easier trails that lead back to the entrance. As I deliberate on which choice serves best my purpose of returning home, the thought of that wink keeps boring into my mind. I relent and opt to accept that invitation. On the way I doubt my choice, the path is steep and I am breaking a sweat even though the air is cool. I wonder if I have fallen for the prank of an old man. I debate whether I should continue following that route or turn around and call it good. And should I chance to overtake the old coot, I'll give him a piece of my mind. The gentle rustling of leaves beckons me to continue. It has been years since I have been this far in the park and I convince myself that perhaps it's worth checking out how it has changed.

I try to catch my breath as I tackle the last stretch of the sloping path. Tired and miffed by the wrong choice, I lean against the trunk of a tree. When my heartbeat slows down to a more regular rate, I resume my ascent. I reach the top of the rise and I freeze in awe: a pyrotechnic explosion of colors in all hues of yellows, oranges and reds bursts into sight. Warmth and delight permeate every part of my spirit. I feel rejuvenated by this unexpected gift to my senses. I stand still, taking in the beauty and letting it soothe my doubts and uncertainties, burnishing the image in my memory. The sun is gliding upward, it is time to go. The gentle incline leads to the main walkway toward the park entrance. I look back, but the small ridge obscures the majestic view. I head toward the arched gate I had absentmindedly crossed on my way in. It is going to be a great fall, however long it lasts.

The Gifts of

Winter

Peace

Rest

Contentment

Winter Is But a Pause

by Carla Guthrie

It is time to rest and grow
Quiet and still,
Slowly put your hand to the quill,
Let the feelings ebb and flow.
Forget the arch of the summer rainbow
Dismiss the sound of the brook descending the hill
As it turns the wheel of the mill,
As it quells the thirst of a doe.

A silent place to ponder,
Pensive and subdued,
About what's past and what lies yonder
Till Spring bringing wonder,
Although by Winter still pursued,
Grows your heart still fonder.

Winter's Dust

by Darlinda Hagens

The dust of winter falls all around.
As we grow older, dust storms soar.
Cold as death, white as snowflakes.
Soon it will come knocking at our door.

Without invitation, it crosses the lines of life.
Sapping strength, challenging medications,
Ignoring prayers and pleas from kin.
Against the dust of winter, who can defend?

Everyone knows it is coming, few stands prepared.
Who wants to trudge winter's dusty trail?
Chilling arms of death, not waiting for permission.
Where it will lead, only God can tell.

Dust descends over the young and old,
Shaping life into its meta-context.
A kiss from tomorrow. Whispered goodbyes.
Before dust settles, Winter beckons. Next.

Winter of Content

by B.S. Adamsons

She startles to consciousness with eyes opening fully when the shrill whistle pierces the paned window. Slowly she draws in a breath as her gaze settles on the soft down comforter embracing her. A calm descends upon a fast-beating heart with the familiarity.

It's only the wind hitting the roof's eave outside, with a parting blow, to give a wake-up call from nature and life. The woman slowly eases her body up from the warmth and reaches for another pillow. She leans it against the cold iron rods of the headframe and pulls the warm covers higher for protection from the outside world's attack.

Through the slats of the dark wood, she feels the muted world of swirling snow. A shiver runs down her body from the empty coldness of the scene and she slides back down into her secure world. She has spent years creating her refuge from a cruel, cold world in a house even older than she is. Walls in a peaceful, gentle blue surround her. A framed poster of wisteria, and a painting of an iris, add calming lavender to the walls. The woods of the antique dresser and night table maintain the house's time of birth and give her a welcomed connection to past generations. Color materializes under the crystal of the lamp's base in the stack of books making her surroundings familiar and comforting.

Suddenly she bolts up, her back as stiff and straight as a stick. Her mind wakens to the present and the day's date. Memories from the past form into images of people celebrating the start of another decade with joyous, smiling faces around her. Greetings appeared in many forms all filled with wishes for continued happiness. A new decade begins in her life today.

But this is her world today – silent, cold, and solitary.

"Good Lord, *stop*. You woke up this morning. That's more than some can say at your age."

She stretches for the phone on the side table and mutes it. Today she will not allow any interruptions from the outside world. Music will be the only sound of a day devoted to herself, alone.

Willy Nelson warns her not to 'let the old man in' and asks, 'how old would you be if you didn't know the day you were born?'

"My new mantra. I still can't believe what decade I've arrived at."

The text icon showed a blank face as she silenced the phone. The outside world appears to be ignoring her day. Has she become as invisible to friends as to the assistants in stores of late? Is she fading into oblivion with increased years?

Spontaneous celebrations have diminished with each passing decade. Today she has total responsibility for changing her mundane routine and spoil herself. Her body awakens at the thought, and she jumps out of the bed's warmth and feels for the softness of silk among the collection of clothes in the closet. Quickly the winter-white body becomes wrapped in shades of summer on an ocean's edge.

"It may be winter in my life's cycle, but I will return my soul to its spring."

The soft movement of the silk, as she walks into the kitchen, returns her to the place she and the garment met. The small boutique was a cave of luxury in Santa Barbara during the film festival. The softness of silk and shades of the nearby ocean captured her soul and continue to mean a bigger world. Festivals in San Sebastian, Cannes and Byron Bay join her memory's meanders. Visions of beaches, flavors of new foods and sounds of foreign languages reappear in her mind. Their joy spreads to her whole being and her steps lighten. Why did she close the door to experiencing the richness of life on the planet through travel adventures?

"Maybe I need to leave winter and book a trip to a new place. Wasn't it only yesterday that I raced through airports? Why did I stop looking for new experiences? Time to live in the day and celebrate being alive. Now where's that champagne I brought back from France?"

The cabinet appears to be lower and deeper than in the past, when she kneels down to retrieve the needed ingredient for a Mimosa. Carefully she places the dulled bottle on the floor before reaching with both hands for the sideboard's edge, and with deliberate focus pulls herself up to stand. A bend is required to retrieve the dark green bottle from the floor.

"Mon Cherie if we are going to make this a proper celebration you better sparkle," she addresses the waiting bottle as she looks around for a polishing cloth. The enjoyment of the moment will be richer if she examines every aspect of the wine's origin and history on the label.

Evaluating each step taken in the new decade the woman smiles with gratitude. There are no grandpa sounds when she pulls her body up to stand, no bones grate, and no sharp pains stop her movement forward. She becomes a researcher on aging and monitors her steps to the counter for steadiness and firmness. Isn't she supposed to be a doddering old woman at this age?

"Those gym visits must be working."

A paper towel returns sparkle to the green bottle again, readying it for a celebration.

"Oh no, is my mind starting to fade? Forgot the crystal flute from the sideboard." A twinge of panic enters her chest as she remembers how her mother's brain faded into nothingness. Has she inherited the same genes? But today this possible fate will not take away the planned joy.

Perched on the solitary barstool at the kitchen counter she savors a long, slow sip of liquid sunshine, and giggles aloud when champagne's bubbles tease her nose.

"I was sittin' here and thinkin' about some old times and some old friends" Don Williams sings to her, in soothing tones. Her mind wanders to one person, but he is on the other side of the world and silent. Others from her past she "would like to see again," but most remain on earth just in words written now and then.

Savoring the golden nectar on her tongue, she glides to her room and pulls out a simple wooden box from under the neatly arranged slacks hanging in the closet. Like a bird rearranging a nest, she snuggles down into the comfort of the unmade bed and opens the box. Colorless folded papers are interrupted by jeweled cards in the box. Each is gently opened. Smiles or puzzled expressions determine whether they are laid to the left or right of her.

Warmth and light from the fireplace push winter's chill from the living room. Reverently she places each sheet on the logs, as on an altar. As words from the past and memories of the writers ascend with the smoke, her mind deposits their essence in her heart.

"Oh, how many of those scribes are no longer on this earth? Time to expand my social circle with a wider range of ages. No more rejecting invites."

Unconsciously she returns to a daily habit, pulls out her phone from a silk pocket.

> Thank you both for the invite. The film festival at the Art Museum sounds great. Would love to come. Will accept the ride offer as my eyes don't like driving at night. Let me treat you to dinner before at one of the fabulous restaurants nearby.

"There! Back to the world of the living and newer friends."

The music accompanies her from the bedroom to the altar for memories with another bundle of cards.

"Keep me in your heart." In soulful tones Warren Zevon, begs to be remembered long after his impending departure. The words ring true. She hears her mother's voice still telling her to aim for a perfectly groomed appearance with constant checks in the mirror. Her father returns after a glance at the ever-expanding book collection on her shelves. She now must carry his torch of devotion to reading.

The Zevon's words remind her of painful memories unexpected times. They are of sitting for hours, holding the hand, and kissing the forehead of a twenty-eight-year-old friend, unconscious after a drug overdose, and then the final kiss.

She presses the rainbow-colored bundle close to her heart, and her parents again return. She was the center of their universe and love as an only child. Before she was ready the situation reversed. She became the parent as she attempted to cajole her father to leave his desk and law books and attend to his physical well-being. Crippling arthritis sent her on searches for ways to keep him proudly independent in his home. But it all was in vain and a vivid image of her mother at his graveside fills her mind, and tears start a slow journey down her own colorless cheek.

A hand wipes away the uninvited moisture and she steps to the mirror to push back fine strands of silver and gold. She pinches her cheeks and brings color to her cheeks.

"Enough! Stop the vanity and yearning for youthfulness. I did wake up, made changes and am in better shape than my parents."

Gym attendances are religious rituals and visits to the farmers' market weekly. She found joy in persuading her mother to take frequent walks around their neighborhoods. She reverted to a childish payback delight for too many bowls of macaroni and cheese, when she taught her mother that vegetables did make a healthy meal. A compulsion to hang onto her remaining parent grew stronger each day. One is never too old to need a parent.

Her mother continued her days of always being well groomed, from early morning through her parade of charitable luncheons and to a lonely cocktail by her TV. Mentions of meeting similar minded ladies for outings grew infrequent, with the continuing days of widowhood. In time, a recounting of events often paused, when a name escaped her mother and she melted into tears of frustration. Soon passing people on the neighborhood streets, were addressed as "darlin", instead of individual names. Some thought the term delightful, and appropriate for the image of the genteel, older lady always dressed in pastels.

A blow of realization struck one morning, when her mother opened the door with a puzzled look and asked, "Yes? What can I do for you, Ma'am?" Her mother's mind had lost decades of gathered treasure, and now was a daily fresh slate, needing reminders to even eat. Numerous doctor visits and tests confirmed that now she was her mother's parent.

Her own life's future possibility stops her dead. Without spouse or child, if ever she is present in the world only physically, who will care for her? Her will needs updating, and her many investments allocated to any necessary future care. Will there be money left to continue work in causes she believes in? She puts a note on her calendar to call her lawyer.

Lovingly she touches her grandparents refurbished cast iron bed. It entered her life when her mother moved into the assisted living home and now is her connection to her family's sparse history. When working, days never were long enough after visits to her mother, to sort through a lifetime of collected memories. Now she has time, in retirement and aloneness.

"I can't let my family fade into oblivion. Time to open Mom's boxes and record the lives lived and lessons learned. Dad taught me independence but was that good? Who said, service to others is the rent you pay for your space on earth? Donating to good causes isn't enough rent. Time to end my selfish existence and give back. Maybe I can make a difference and mentor someone young."

The remaining treasured cards sink into their new home of a velvet box, still fragrant from past chocolates. Slowly she returns to the counter and picks up the nearly full glass of mimosa as Willy Nelson and Ray Charles announce that "It was a very good year."

242   CELEBRATING THE SEASONS

"I'll drink to that," she says aloud and sinks back onto the barstool.

Seventeen was certainly a good age. Every day she woke excited about new friends and exploring life. Twenty-one started the search for a life partner. Many memorable romances ensued, but her need for independence always stood in the way. Thirty-five opened a world of travel and living a privileged life, because of career successes. The expanding smile shows no regrets about choosing an independent lifestyle, only joy about the richness of experiences and friends made.

As she replaces an empty glass on the counter, a beam of sunlight strikes the crystal, throwing a rainbow onto the wall, as the words of a song drift through the space.

"The color of the rainbow so pretty in the sky…"

She glances past it to the unshaded window. The snow has given way to a clear blue sky. The world outside is fresh and new.

"What a wonderful world, what a wonderful world," fades into strings and a ukulele and then silence.

"Yes, it is, and it does not have a definitive timeline that everyone must adhere to. Flowers bloom and fade on their own schedules and do not concern themselves about fitting into a particular season. So can I."

"Time to live fully the day given. Winter stops nothing. I am content."

Changing Roles

by E.H. McEachern

"Just a little more.... almost there... almost there." The corner of the mystery photo beckoned beguilingly from the top shelf of the bookcase. Anne's fingertips brushed against it. She stretched her fingers and stood up even higher on her tiptoes, but her hope of retrieving the errant photo was too great a challenge for the laws of gravity. Anne's step stool shot out from under her feet, and rocketed into the end table. The old lamp crashed to the floor and shattered into a thousand pieces, along with everything else on the table. Anne followed suit just a hair's breadth later.

Even before the sounds ceased reverberating, Joe flew down the old stairway, his face swollen, eyes barely open and his hair as askew as the scarecrow in the dormant west-side vegetable garden patch.

He took in the chaos with one glance, and rushed to Anne's side. "Good God, woman, it's two in the morning.... what happened? Are you okay?"

Anne plopped her head back down to the floor, "Do I look okay?" Pains in her left calf, initially hidden within the adrenalin rush of the fall, asserted themselves with a vengeance. Anne groaned and grimaced, "Damn Joe, better call an ambulance."

As Anne lay flat out amid the remnants of her formerly cozy living room, she watched the photo she so diligently sought release its hold from the top shelf and drift slowly down to rest in the middle of her chest. Staring back at her was the sepia-colored portrait of a young boy, probably around twelve years old, dressed in pioneer garb and holding a shotgun that was as tall as he. On the back it read, "Henry Rafferty, June 1889."

After two weeks of sitting in her favorite chair with her broken and casted leg up, or on the couch with her leg up, or at the kitchen table with her leg up, Anne was ready to sign herself into a mental ward. She bemoaned the loss of her antique lamp and the other old trivial pieces that had made a home on her defunct end table. Wisely, her family gave her a wide berth as they tiptoed around her silently.

"It's almost my birthday and I can't do a darn thing. I've got cooking to take care of, house to clean, boxes to pack and, worst of all, we've got to figure out how to break the news to the family," she moaned.

"Don't worry, it'll all work out," Joe assured her.

"That's easy for you to say. All you have to do is eat."

Joe didn't pursue what was sure to be another fit of self-pity. Instead, he went out to the back porch and retrieved two large boxes, filled with old photos, journals and newspaper clippings.

"Since you took so much trouble getting that old photo down from the top shelf, I thought you might be interested in seeing the other stuff that went with it. I found all this," his hands spread wide across the papers, "in the attic and it looked pretty interesting. I thought since you're not able to get up and around..." Anne glared at her husband. Joe ignored her as he continued, "You might give these old papers a once-over and see what you find."

Anne harumphed, folded her arms across her chest and turned her head. "Sure, like I have time to mess with ancient history when the whole world is falling apart. I have so much to do and can't do any of it. I still don't see how we're going to tell the kids about what we're planning. I just don't know how they will take it."

And that, Joe thought, was the real issue.

Joe shook his head, kissed his wife on the top of hers and headed out the door. After a few minutes of sitting in the silence, Anne gazed over at the boxes. The old, battered sheets beckoned and Anne's innate good humor and curiosity finally won out. She soon found herself sorting the different documents, newspaper clippings and journals into some sort of order. Finally, a timeline emerged. The hours passed and Anne found herself immersed in the history and personal stories of those who owned their land long before she and Joe called it home.

The earliest paper tale began with the Oklahoma Land Run on April 22, 1889. An estimated 50,000 people vied for parts of a two-million-acre land area. Under the U. S. Homestead Act of 1862, individuals were able to stake out 160 acres at no cost. After living on the property for five years and making improvements, the stakeholder would gain title to the land. Even women, who could not yet legally vote in national elections, could participate. The only restriction was that the person filing must be 21 years or older or head of a household.

One such story unfolded through the letters exchanged between Eileen McDonald and her aunt, Maureen. The letters were oddly discolored, written on very thin paper and tied together with a piece of frayed twine. Months, and sometimes years, separated

the pieces of correspondence, yet Anne was able to put
it into a reasonable story.

January 5, 1889

Abilene, Kansas

Dear Aunt Maureen,

*I have received this day the most unusual letter and
map from a Sgt. Wilbur Kane. I am copying it for
you. It offers hope for a better future for myself and
the children, but I am somewhat skeptical of its
contents. To do as he suggests would mean
uprooting the family and heading out into the
unknown.*

*Please read Sgt. Kane's letter. Do you know
anything of this gentleman or his relationship with
Grandfather during the war? Shall I stake the
future of my family on his recommendation? As
you know, life has been quite difficult since my dear
husband, Henry, passed. We have barely been
surviving, and I would not wish to make a
disastrous decision that would leave us in more
desperate circumstances, nor do I wish to ignore a
chance for a better life.*

Your loving niece

Eleanor McDonald

Enclosed letter copy

November, 1888

Dear Mrs. McDonald,

I write to you today from my sick bed in hopes this letter will reach you in good time. I want to make things right before I meet my Maker.

I understand that you and your family have fallen upon hard times after the death of your husband. I would like to share with you a gift that I had originally wanted to keep for myself, but as I am near death from the devil consumption, I will not be able to make that happen for me.

I will, however, be able to keep a promise made to your grandfather, Col. Benjamin Riley, during the war which wrest our country apart. Col. Riley was a fine man, upright and fair in his dealing with his men, courageous in battle and, I am proud to say, a real friend. He saved me and his men on many an occasion. Sadly, the Battle of Vicksburg cost him dearly. I held him as he breathed his last and he asked only that I look out for his family.

Regretfully, I have not lived up to that promise, but circumstances and the Good Lord have given me one final chance to do so.

From 1885 until 1888 I was one of the land surveyors for the acres in Oklahoma territory that will open for homesteading sometime in the next few months. During that time, I found a valley, the most beautiful on God's green earth. Although I did stake it for the land run, I mapped it in such a way that it showed only a very long route to get there. There is a much faster way, and I carefully drew this shortcut, hoping I would be able to claim that pristine valley for myself.

I am placing that map in this letter and pray that you can find and claim it for yourself. I know it will be like the promised land for you and will allow me to hold my head high when I once again meet the Colonel.

Very sincerely,

Sgt Wilbur Kane

5th Kansas Cavalry

Apparently, the McDonalds decided to roll the dice and make for Oklahoma territory, because the next letter read:

May 25, 1889

Oklahoma Territory

My dear Aunt Maureen,

By the light of our campfire, I write to you. This is the first chance I have had to tell you Henry, Jr. and I are well, having successfully found the blessed spot of land with water, decent soil and space. Sister Carolyn and her husband Matthew accompanied us, as they, too, were seeking a better life. I think the good Lord looked upon us when he sent the letter from Sgt. Riley. His map led to this very spot and because the shortcut was so well disguised, we had no others trying to outrun us or steal the stake from us. They probably thought we were just some stupid Easterners, not knowing anything about the land. (As I am sure we would have been without divine help.) We each staked out 160 acres – side by-side.

The day of the run was Monday, April 22. I have never seen so many people and so many conveyances all together in one place. People on horseback, in wagons, even some running on foot. Everybody had a rifle in hand. We choked on the dust when the soldier's horn sounded at noon and we launched into the chaos as fast as we could.

As soon as we build a home, we will bring the rest of the children. I am sending you a photograph of Henry and his rifle. He is so proud and has already assumed his role as "man of the house," even though he is only twelve years old.

We bless Sgt. Kane each night in our prayers.

Your loving niece,

Eileen McDonald

Anne mused, "So that's how it all began."

The next document was a death certificate dated December 1917 for Henry Benjamin McDonald, III, age 19. Son of Henry B. McDonald and Sarah James.

Served honorably in France and Belgium. Casualty of the Great War.

The next group of papers included the 1940 death certificate for Henry B. McDonald, Jr. who was shot to death by his cousin, Axle Sims. According to the newspaper clippings and the transcript of Sims murder trial, the two cousins quarreled over property lines and water rights between the adjacent ranches. The quarrel had lasted decades, and finally Sims had had enough. One moonless night, he bushwacked McDonald and shot him dead. There was no doubt that Sims was guilty. He even said McDonald deserved it. As is in true western lore, Sims was quickly convicted and hanged. Since Sims had no other relatives and could not gain from murdering his cousin, the Sims property was awarded to Samuel McDonald, eldest surviving son of Henry.

Now, Samuel McDonald was a name Anne recognized from her family stories. She knew he had died young, but not because he was a soldier in WWII. Since the family farmed and raised livestock, Samuel was deferred from the draft because his occupation was deemed essential to the war effort. However, because of the shortage of labor for the farm, Samuel would often work long hours with old and inefficient equipment. It was one of these old and inefficient tractors that rolled over him one late evening and ended his life.

Anne turned over the next document in the stack. Her hand sprung to her chest and tears suddenly moistened the corners of her eyes. Now, this was a name she knew very well. It was that of her Uncle Charlie. When Anne was still a child, her Uncle Charlie had fought in the Vietnamese War. He came home a different person. When he left for boot camp, he was a happy, carefree young man, but when he returned, the spark of life had left him. In the period of just more than one year, he had become a morose, cynical, dysfunctional old man living in a young man's body. It wasn't too long after that that Uncle Charlie committed suicide. The family was devastated.

Anne remembered one specific time when Charlie sat staring at the silver star he had won in the conflict. Anne asked what he did to earn the medal and Charlie said, "Well sweetheart, I guess I got this because I was the only one who lived." Now she read of the heroic efforts Charlie had made to save his fellow soldiers – efforts that proved to be in vain. Everyone involved in the ambush had been killed – all but Charlie. It was incredibly sad to think of her uncle and the trauma he must have endured in that senseless war. Her heart ached for him.

As the farms passed down the next generations, ownership ended with Anne McDonald Pearson herself. The parameters of the farm changed over time; some land purchased; other parts sold. But still, the center of it all was the original land grant staked out during the Oklahoma Land Run of 1889.

For a long time, Anne sat in the comfort of her living room, thinking of the people and the years that had passed on this land, of the hardships, the drama and joy that had played out all around her. And even before the Oklahoma land run, were the many unwritten stories of the native people who lived, farmed, hunted or traversed this beautiful valley. One season to another – one year to another, the people and their dreams may have differed, but the land remained as changeless as it had always been.

As the day's shadows lengthened and dissolved into twilight, Anne finally understood that she and her family were only a small part of the history of this valley. Joe was right; everything would be okay. A sense of peace enveloped her like a warm well-worn and loved blanket.

Anne's birthday and the day of the big announcement dawned. Everyone noticed Anne's change in attitude, even though her leg was still encapsulated and it still itched like crazy. She didn't know how the kids would take the news that she and Joe would soon be moving to Florida and leaving the running of the farm to them. But she no longer feared what was ahead.

Joe heard the tires crunch in the gravel outside the back door. Their eldest, Mark, bundled up against the cold December wind ploughed into the kitchen carrying gift-wrapped presents. "My goodness, Mark, did you buy out the store?" was his mother's comment. Tumbling in after Mark came the twins and his wife, Marty, holding their one-year-old closely to her chest.

Mary came in next. Since Anne was still having trouble getting around easily, Joe had assigned Mary the responsibility of bringing take-out for the birthday party. And, as always, Mary had gone overboard. The adults and the twins emptied Mary's SUV. The food was hot, smelled wonderful and, according to the twins, everyone was starving. Especially for birthday cake.

"Hey guys," Joe shouted over the hullabaloo. "We need to wait until Jess gets here. Grandma and I have something important to tell you, and…"

Mark quipped, "Oh. You mean about moving to Florida and leaving the farm for Jess to run?"

Mary chimed in, "Yeah, I thought that had already been decided. I'm sure not going to be a farm girl."

Joe and Anne looked at each other with expressions of astonishment and disbelief. "How did you know?"

"Well, Dad, you have been doing a lot of cleaning out, packing, tying up loose ends, making sure everything is legally copacetic. What else could it be? "You know, we lawyers are pretty observant and smart. I'm guessing you want me to handle the legal stuff, and Mary to handle the finances. Jess may be a great farmer, but he sure has some holes in his training." Mark laughed.

If Joe's jaw could have dropped any lower, it would have.

His sister, Mary, rolled her eyes and elbowed Mark in the ribs. "I found out from the Stewarts. Their mom and dad moved out there a couple of years ago and they told Emma how excited they were that you and dad had finally decided to join them in the "good life." Farming is tough and you both deserve to take it a little easier. Plus, you've been trying to hand off so many of the 'family treasures' for months. Could anything be more obvious?"

Anne was speechless.

Tires squealed outside and came to a sudden halt. The kitchen door flew open and a blast of frigid, Oklahoma wind poured through the kitchen. Their youngest, Jess, stood there with his weathered green John Deere hat in his hand. "Mom, Dad, is it true? Are you really moving to Florida? I was just down at the Co-op and Fred Zane said you were going to...." He looked around.

The room broke into a jumble of laughter and tears. Everyone hugged one another. Even the kids joined in, although they weren't sure what was so funny.

Jess just stood there, bewildered.

Later that night, after everyone had gone home to contemplate the new family reality, Joe asked Anne why she had suddenly seemed so at peace. Anne thought a minute and then said, "it took reading about all those people who lived here before to help me understand that our upcoming transition was not a time for trepidation but celebration. Moving on is just a part of life – like the changing of seasons, the changing of life roles ...it's as nature intends it to be.

Some transitions are difficult, others smooth. Some happen routinely, others seemingly out of sync or wreathed in tragedy. But they always happen – one generation to the next – one season to the next."

Then she smiled, "And at the end of one comes the promise of a new beginning."

The Midnight Blue Velvet Dress

by Donna Castle Richardson

Saturday evening of my ninth Christmas we drove into the parking lot of the little white church with a steeple in rural Oklahoma just West of the university town where my father had finished college on the GI bill the year before. The GI bill helped pay for his education because of his army service during World War II. The Oklahoma Territorial Legislature established the University in 1901 as the Southwestern Normal School and later Southwestern State Teachers College in May of 1921.

My Daddy was the second generation in his family to earn a teaching certificate at the teacher's college. I would be the third generation to attend the same college and complete my degree in teacher education. My grandfather had earned a lifetime teaching certificate at the college and believed teaching was God's work.

As we drove up to the church, my friends ran out to meet us. My daddy had been the minister at the church over the past year and one half and we were going to have our first Christmas celebration together. This is one of the best memories of my childhood. The love and friendship that I experienced that evening in that little white church remains a highlight of my childhood.

Old memories flooded my mind as I met my two best friends and we played and talked together sharing the warm bond of friendship that happens after spending special times together. Janie and Judy were the girls my age at the church, and we had become friends.

At church I had discovered Janie was a different person. I had avoided her in first grade where we went to school in the original little white four room schoolhouse in the University town that housed two first and second grades. She had been in second grade and considered a playground bully. At church, I discovered she was different and sorry about being a bully. We became good friends.

Janie and I had spent many afternoons together after Sunday morning church service. At her house we would have a wonderful home cooked lunch then go to the creek and explore. The memories of exploring the creek and the discovery and adventure of observing the beautiful rocks and pebbles as we looked at them was a highlight of our Sunday afternoons. Just being close to nature and enjoying the shelter under the tree lined creek as the water trickled through was the highpoint of the afternoon before we went back to church in the evening to hear my Daddy preach.

Judy was my other friend. We had bonded and enjoyed each other over her beautiful collection of dolls. I only had two dolls while Judy had an enormous collection. She was a special child because she had been a what they called at that time a late in life baby. Her parents had three older grown children, but Judy was special because she was born to her parents later in life. She was a delightful person who was pretty and petite but best of all kind and loving. We both enjoyed playing with her doll collection.

Christmas evening, we sat together to enjoy the Christmas service that began with the singing of Christmas hymns. In the Baptist Church, they always start out with music to get us relaxed, involved, and set a spiritual mood for the minister's message. Daddy of course told the Christmas story about Jesus' birth and some people shared their gratitude for the year.

After the service finished, the congregation had a special treat for our family. They gave us each a gift. My gift was a beautiful midnight blue velvet dress with a white lace collar. I know there was a great deal of love in the selection and giving of that exquisite dress. It was the most beautiful dress that I had ever seen. I enjoyed wearing it on many future occasions. Today from the special memory, my favorite clothes are velvet. Each winter when it is cold out, I always want to wear velvet because it keeps me warm and reminds me of the love expressed in a little rural church from the wonderful congregation.

A Word to the Wise is Sufficient

Change is

Inevitable

Every Season Brings Its

Special Gifts

verbum sap sapienti est

by Holly Jahangiri

Barefoot, she runs across the verdant veldt,
rumble-tumble falls down polished, moss-slick
crags and crannies, sparkling translucent jade.
Tumultuous her joy - as overhead
the stately redwoods, timeless cedars fly.
Up, up into the cobalt sky she leaps -
to soar - an eagle o'er the canopy
of lush, exotic, fragrant blooming things.
And at her touch, her kiss, each unripe fruit
attains Spring's first blush and yields its sweetness.
Capricious whims, lightning quick to anger -
verbum sap sapienti est. Thick smoke,
Hell's flames, her ire - yet blackened, charred -
new life still finds a way, as emerald eyes
peek through the cooling ashes of her rage
and blinking up, there sprouts a brand-new day.

About the Authors

B.S. Adamsons

B.S. Adamsons started her writing path in third grade, when Mother Francis Xavier pointed to a print on the classroom's back wall and commanded – "Write a story."

In the many decades since, writing has taken many different forms. Philosophical thoughts were submitted to a newspaper's Teen Page with the goal of spreading ideas and earning pocket money as well. College provided opportunities to write skits for her fellow students to perform. Parenthood required the skill of written persuasions for Letters to the Editor or school boards.

Years at a hometown newspaper provided the opportunity for writing advice columns and to promote "Yard of the Week" with creative descriptions of winning gardens.

Over the years, fancy notebooks and loose papers filled drawers, after places visited and people met, till a new life-decade began and Sister Francis Xavier's words rang out:

"Write a story."

Dorothy Cady

Dorothy Cady lives in Oklahoma and has written for various publications, including *Backwoods Home Magazine*, *KeyBytes*, *Writopia*, and *The Report*. She's been a technical writer for over two decades, and has published books with McGraw-Hill Osborne, New Riders Publishing, Que books, and Macmillan Computer Publishing. Cady also writes and develops online courses, and served as Treasurer/Webmaster of the Oklahoma Writers Federation, Inc. before becoming the organization's President in 2005-2006. Dorothy holds a degree of Master of General Education and a Master of Fine Arts in Creative Writing.

Carla Guthrie

Carla Guthrie has cultivated her passion for writing since first grade, when her teacher patiently guided her hand to form letters. One of the poems she wrote in third grade was chosen and published by a children's magazine. In college she won first place in the *Soundings Literary Journal* contest with her short story The Master's Hand. After a two-decade hiatus spent raising and teaching her four boys, she is ready to share her stories with the world once again. Hailing from Florence, Italy and longtime resident of Oklahoma she enjoys writing both in Italian and English to evoke emotions and entertain readers with thought provoking tales.

Darlinda Hagens

Darlinda Hagens enjoys writing Christian Fiction Romance. Her soon-to-be released novel, *Fighting For Faith*, was birthed from Hebrews 11:1—Now faith is the substance of things hoped for, the evidence of things not seen. The story points out that Christians are not perfect. Unquestionably, we make mistakes. And sometimes, regardless of how loud and long we pray, God does not always say yes. The no's are a part of the faith walk, believing even when we don't see the way out.

Although Darlinda is a bit of an introvert, she loves meeting people and making new friends. However, she arose from her self-proclaimed shyness (most who know her do not agree with the admission) long enough to enter a few writing contests.

In 2019, her poem "Final Emotions" won third place in OWFI's annual writing contest. Her essay "What Do You See When You Look At Him" won first place in OWFI's 2020 contest.

As a lifelong Oklahoman, Darlinda enjoys traveling. You will find some of the wonderful places she has visited in her stories.

Darlinda writes Christian Romance as a tool to glorify God, hoping to inspire others to step out in faith and put their trust in Him, too.

Holly Jahangiri

Holly Jahangiri is the author of *Trockle*; *A Puppy, Not a Guppy*; and *A New Leaf for Lyle*. She draws inspiration from her family, from her own childhood adventures (some of which only happened in her overactive imagination), and from readers both young and young at heart. She lives in Houston, Texas, with her husband, J.J., whose love and encouragement make writing books twice the fun.

Eva M. Mahoney

Eva M. Mahoney has been writing since she was in elementary school. She wrote her first story in third grade entitled, "The Rabbit Who Wouldn't Deliver." She had three articles published in *The Buffalo News* while she was still in high school. Several decades later, Eva writes mostly in the Mainstream genre. She does focus much of her writing on humor. She won an Honorable Mention in the OWFI Literary Competition in 2020 for her humor blog entitled Friendship Application. (Eva does not require potential friends to complete a friendship application.) In her short story here, "No Trip to Oz," her main character, Yaz, plays a reoccurring role in a series of short stories yet to be published. Eva lives with her husband, Phil and their weeniepoo, Pepe in Edmond, Oklahoma.

E.H. McEachern

Evelyn McEachern holds a doctorate in Higher Education Administration from Oklahoma State University. Serving as a teacher, administrator and as an Assistant Vice-President, she retired from academic life after more than thirty years of serving students.

Being energetic and focused, Dr. McEachern has found retirement to be a springboard for various ventures and activities including charity fund raising, traveling, and miniature doll house construction.

The Jenny Tallchief series is the result of some two years of thoughtful research and planning.

Dr. McEachern and her husband live in Edmond, Oklahoma where she continues to spoil their Lhasa Apso, Maggie.

Donna Castle Richardson, Ed.D.

Donna Castle Richardson, Ed.D. serves as the CEO of Educational Dynamics, LLC. She previously served as the Director of the Central Comprehensive Center, one of 15 Comprehensive Centers providing technical assistance with funding from the United States Department of Education through the University of Oklahoma. She also served as the Director of EDUTAS at OU. She is a Professor Emeritus in the Department of Education at Oklahoma City University (OCU) where she designed and directed the teacher certification program in Early Childhood and directed the Elementary Education. She taught courses in early childhood education, curriculum, children's literature, emergent literacy, and reading development. She mentored teachers during their first year of teaching.

She has developed a Reading with Children Series for parents, grandparents, and early childhood educators that focus on informing parents, grandparents, and early childhood educators on how to create a stimulating learning environment for children during the early years. Her *Activities & Ideas for Enhancing Young Children's Language* won the 2022 Oklahoma Writers Federation, Inc 2022 Published Book – Non-Fiction award. The series has two additional adult handbooks *Teaching Your Child to Read Naturally Parenting Handbook* and *Teaching Alphabet Letters and Sounds with Meaning*. To complete the series, she wrote three children's books to assist adults in how to read using interactive reading techniques to young children reading strategies and letters and sounds in context. Three of the author's children's books, *The Teeny Tiny Tadpole*, *Little Lilly Ladybug*, and *Birds Being Birds*, serve as companions to the parenting handbooks to give young children a head start in reading.

Dr. Richardson's interest in family literacy research, early reading, children's literature, language development, and school improvement led to national recognition. She evaluated the Oklahoma City Public Schools' Even Start project in which her research and the project design was validated by the U.S. Department of Education's National Diffusion Network and awarded a National Dissemination Grant to fund national dissemination. Her Reading Discovery Tutor Training program was highlighted as one of ten programs featured in the U.S. Department of Education's best practices document So That Every Child Can Read...America Reads Community and Tutoring Projects.

Donna is married to Don Ray Richardson. Their home is in Edmond, Oklahoma. They have two married children and five grandchildren who live in Denver, Colorado.

Joe Scavetti

Joe Scavetti comes from a long line of story tellers. At an early age, he learned the importance of humor, surprise, and timing in relating a good tale.

Since retiring from a career in human resources and higher education administration, Scavetti now has more time to devote to his favorite hobby – writing.

Having an outgoing personality, typical of those born in the sign of Leo, Joe becomes the center of most groups. He is usually found telling jokes, spinning yarns, or making light of situations that have become too serious.

Scavetti's quick wit and creative imagination become evident in this time-travel thriller, Reflections of the Future.

Joe Scavetti believes that life is worth living and tries to enjoy every minute of it. He and his wife, Evelyn, currently reside in Edmond, Oklahoma, a suburb of Oklahoma City.

Lightning Source UK Ltd.
Milton Keynes UK
UKHW020039110123
415109UK00015B/830